THE STI⊓

NEW WRITERS

Issue 40 Volume 1... · Summer 2019

'… God has specially appointed me to this city, so as though it were a large thoroughbred horse which because of its great size is inclined to be lazy and needs the stimulation of some stinging fly…'

—Plato, *The Last Days of Socrates*

The Stinging Fly
new writers, new writing
PO Box 6016, Dublin 1
info@stingingfly.org

Editor: Danny Denton

Publisher
Declan Meade

Poetry Editor
Cal Doyle

Design & Layout
Fergal Condon

Assistant Editor
Sara O'Rourke

Eagarthóir Filíochta
Aifric MacAodha

Website
Ian Maleney

Contributing Editors
Mia Gallagher, Lisa McInerney, Thomas Morris and Sally Rooney

Printed by Walsh Colour Print, County Kerry

ISBN 978-1-906539-79-5   ISSN 1393-5690

The Stinging Fly gratefully acknowledges the support of The Arts Council/
An Chomhairle Ealaíon.

NEW FICTION

BORDER VOICES

The Stinging Fly was established in 1997 to publish and promote
the best new Irish and international writing.

Published twice a year, we welcome submissions on a regular basis.

The next open submission window is from
December 2nd 2019 to January 16th 2020.

Online submissions only. Please read the submission guidelines on our website.

Keep in touch: sign up to our email newsletter, become a fan on Facebook, or follow us on Twitter
for regular updates about our publications, podcasts, workshops and events.

stingingfly.org | facebook.com/StingingFly | @stingingfly

Editorial

In the basement of The Clark County Historical Museum in Vancouver, Washington, there is an underground library, run by a man named John F. Barber. It's called The Brautigan Library, and what's special about The Brautigan Library is that its collection is composed entirely of unpublished manuscripts. There are over three hundred there, each one submitted by its author and free to be read by anyone who visits. The Brautigan Library wasn't always in a basement; it was originally the brainchild of Todd Lockwood, who opened the door of this special place in 1990, on Lower College Street in Vermont. At first, the manuscripts were stacked between two jars of mayonnaise on a shelf in the small, high-ceilinged space that Lockwood called a library. Then the space became larger, and busier, as people came and handed over their dreams, visions, words, stories and theories in manuscript form. Of course the library's name is a clue to its deeper origins. Lockwood got the idea for his library having read *The Abortion*, by Richard Brautigan, a novel about a librarian who runs a library for… unpublished manuscripts. So, this real-life library for unpublished work has its foundation in the notions and visions of a writer, themselves distilled into a (at one time, unpublished) manuscript. There is something fitting, circular and endlessly affirming about all that, and, for me, it's an important notional shift from the emphasis on 'getting published' to an emphasis on producing creative work for the world.

It was just these sorts of dreams and notions and visions and theories—their irrepressibility and variety—that so impressed and affected me in reading the submissions for this Summer 2019 issue of *The Stinging Fly*. We received over 1500 submissions this time around: 982 were short stories (which I read); 603 were poetry (which Cal Doyle read), and we also received a number of essay queries. What a gift to have been given: the chance to read from each of these, to engage with pieces of art that each writer had dreamed and schemed and committed to the page.

Thomas Morris, in a foreword to *Quarryman IV* (published out of UCC last year), referred to the pieces within it as 'acts of love'. I agree with this way of thinking about prose and poetry, and while it wasn't always easy and while I wasn't always mad about particular submissions in and of themselves, I was blown away by the sheer effort and inventiveness and care that went into each submission. It was a wonder to realise that so many people—all over the world, from various backgrounds and out of myriad experiences—are committed to making imaginative work, and making it well, and sending it out. What a cool thing to be a part of!

And dizzying. I read my entries from January 9th to around March 12th. I spent that time reading a ludicrous amount, and found myself dreaming the stories and essays, filing scenes from them as memories (incorrectly). I became weirdly inhabited by them too: one minute I was in a waiting room in Cairo; another I was at a house party in Southeast London. I must have drank in a couple of hundred pubs, and conversed with (or eavesdropped on) thousands of people; I met Beyoncé during a power cut at a Nigerian radio station; I convinced myself that someone I knew (actually) was living in their car, before I realised I was thinking of a submission I'd read. All in a couple of months, all through that wonderful act of telepathy we call reading.

Of course, we couldn't accept every piece—that's the shitty part—and, of course, not every piece was ready for publication, but regardless, this many people committing these acts of love towards language, towards readers, is utterly brilliant, and I'm thankful to have read each of them. So this is to salute everyone who commits dreams, visions, words, stories and theories to the page, and who sends those works out for others to read. And this is also to say that what's here in this document, in your hands, is only a sliver of the love, variety and raw *bearing of witness* we received.

A final thing to say about putting together this issue is that *The Stinging Fly* is a team of people (see our publication page for details), and it has been marvellous and educational and so much fun to engage with them all, discussing the merits of the work and layout and look; talking, arguing, sharing ideas, trying to make the best decisions. A fundamental joy of art is talking about the work, and ultimately sharing it with others, so my thanks to the team for their rich input in that regard, to everyone who submitted work, and to you, the reader, who completes the work of making something by taking it into your hands and giving it life.

Danny Denton
May 2019

Harpies

Dizz Tate

Jess and I are at the pub. It is Halloween in 2013. We are feeling the light mellow drunk that falls between pints three and four. We are at the stage of Big Opinions About Books. At pint four, we'll be at politics. At five, we'll start drinking tequila and we'll talk about sex. At pint six, I stop remembering. But we are at pint three. I am in love with the power of my own coherence.

'I am so over people being writers in novels,' says Jess.

Her nails are three inches long, fire-engine red, honed to a sharp point that would be ideal for scooping out an eyeball. We are sitting in the pub opposite our university. It is 5 PM. We are bitching. We are the bitches of the creative writing workshop. We catch each other's eyes when the others read, a glint of malice and ego and envy, thinking that even our shittiest work will be read more than theirs. Maybe. Jess is good, and I've read enough to pretend to be. I'm eighteen, she is twenty-five. She's smart in an old way. When she sat down next to me the first day of university, I felt the same kind of heat I did in Year 9 when Georgia May Cooper picked me as the girl to go with her to get sunbeds on Wednesdays after school, or in Year 10 when Laura Nottingham drew her eyeliner on me in the toilets during lunch, or in sixth form when Amy Palamartschuk told me to skip school with her for the first time to roll cigarettes and turn our backs on boys. The brightening effects. Hot, cool girls paying attention to me is the strongest of my many weaknesses, and they've never been that hard to attract. I am small, brunette, and round. I crouch next to beauties like a full stop. I *accentuate*.

'Yeah, I hate reading about writers,' I agree.

'It's the self-awareness of it,' she says. 'Also, like, you just know they're really boring and have nothing better to write about except themselves. It's like, get a life, you know.'

'Yeah,' I say, pointlessly.

We look around the pub. Terrible prints are fitted puzzle-like around the walls: a reprint of the Southern Gothic; a small photograph of a kitten in a milk jug; a framed photo of Cilla Black. The purple velvet of the seats is scratched and balding, with tiny black age spots of indeterminable origin. We have discussed the décor at length. The only other occupant of the pub is an old man with his hand gnarled around a pint gone flat. His nose is humped. He looks like a drawing in a Roahl Dahl book. I think about saying this to Jess but I have learned she prefers silences to what she calls my pixie dreamgirl shit.

'Hey,' she says. She snaps her fingers and I snap to attention. We are back to bitching.

'What did you think of Delilah's poem?' she says. She jabs one of her long nails down her throat, far enough back that any unpractised girl would gag. She pulls it out cleanly. 'Am I right or am I right?' she says.

Delilah is a girl in our class who is writing a long sequence of poems about a group of girls in a mental hospital. At first, the girls are normal and just seem to sleep and cry a lot, but then the poems get weird. The girls start growing. They float around the ward, never flying, but hovering on the walls, stuck like flies when they sense a swatting. They sound creepy, the girls, like they are about to do something terrible. The poems make me feel sick, like I want to plug my ears, especially when Delilah reads them out loud, slowly, like she is convinced of their importance. She has given all the girls curly pastel-coloured hair. She calls their white, uniform pyjamas wedding dresses.

Jess asked her during workshop: 'Why do you keep calling them wedding dresses? I think you should call them what they are. Like, they're in a hospital, right? Why don't you just say that?'

The rest of us politely pretend that the creator of whoever's work we are discussing has evaporated when we speak, offering up vague comparisons and saying things like, 'I liked it but I don't know if I got it completely'. Jess always stares directly at the writer and asks them questions even though they aren't allowed to talk. Today, Delilah continued to furiously doodle over her manuscript, refusing to look to her left at Jess, who was getting closer and closer to talking directly in her ear. I could see why Delilah was pissed. Delilah is a large girl, spotty, with thick hair that sticks out of her head like two book ends. She's been dealt the card of hard adjectives from God. Jess is beautiful, the kind of beauty that didn't require Accutane or braces.

Still, Jess told me drunk once that she had had an eating disorder bad enough that she was in the kind of hospital Delilah was now lyrically describing.

'Were you starving or making yourself sick or both?' I asked her. She poked me hard in the chest with one of her nails. It hurt. She said, 'That's what I like about you. You don't sympathise, you just ask what you want to know.'

I didn't know what to say so I just nodded. I figured she was making herself sick. Halfway through nights at the pub when we drank so much we couldn't talk, we'd go eat cheesy chips and then throw up together in the alley behind the shop. She did it with the precision and grace of routine, while I retched and shuddered my way to release. We called it purging. In our drunken state, sometimes we yelled 'Amen!' after, or 'Praise Jesus!' in Southern drawls. Then we'd go back to the pub.

'Do you think Teach liked it?' asks Jess now.

'He likes all the poets,' I say. 'He knows they need all the luck they can get.'

She laughs and I feel the pleasantness of her admiration. Jess likes when I am mean.

Our creative writing teacher is a terrified twenty-something with glasses thick enough that his eyes seem to be a long distance away. He always seems certain and scared that one of us is about to seduce him against his will. We are all girls in the creative writing class and we all seem to love him in the same starved and disappointed way. I have worked very hard this month following Jess around to parties but there don't seem to be any upcoming tumultuous love affairs for me. There are just the boys, the ones who wait up in kitchens and gardens, freezing, until it is just the two of you, mumbling drunken inanities, and then there is hope and sweat and holding, and then you talk about what you're scared of, how you don't think your parents ever loved you, really. You ask each other what your bodies look like, in whispers you remember later with a vague sense of shame. Either this is enough, or you have the disappointed bored streak in you that makes you spiteful, makes you want to fuck the teacher or your boss or the married guy, because you've read the books and seen the movies and listened to the music, and you know love is a lot of things, but it isn't supposed to be easy. I am going to be one of those, I guess. In my teacher's office hours, I lean further over the desk while he builds a wall of books between us. Then he hands me my story and says something lacking in passion but ultimately pretty useful, like not to use so many similes and to end the story halfway through.

'I think that'll help give it a bit of life,' he says, peering at me over his glasses and his books. Then I take my dead foetus of a story in the crook of my arm until I'm out on the college green, where I enjoy screwing it up dramatically into the bin and rolling a fat loose cigarette, relighting it every five seconds against the wind of the day, and thinking fuck you, in the way Jess says it, like it is affection, a gift, an admiring I love you, fuuuuck you, babe. Then I go back to my sad little room to see one of the few boys I have managed to take home from parties, and he'll offer me his armpit, ask if I want to watch *Peep Show* or eat a fishcake. This is my life so far at university.

'Delilah's poem would be good if she didn't say everything three times,' I say. I feel the beer stirring in my gut, as if to chastise me, tell me what I already know. *You are full of shit.* It's true. What do I know about being in a mental hospital? What do I know about anything? All my stories are dead.

Jess laughs and I watch her eat the last of the chilli crisps, nails scrawling in the plastic packet for the crumbs. Jess writes stories about hot girls loving each other, hating each other, hot girls turning into old, lukewarm girls. They are good, everyone knows it. When she speaks, we all perk up our ears to listen. She is also the only hot girl in the class. The rest of us aren't bad, but we're tepid, tap water. Jess is tequila, sour lemon, oil-spit in the hot frying pan. Jess never has boyfriends or girlfriends. The rest of us have someone who comes and gets us from the pub eventually, or someone we try to get off with at the end of the night. Jess doesn't seem to like anyone except me and even me she tires of. When the pubs close, I imagine she stalks the streets like a real writer, her hands raised, her nails deathly pointed warnings, to think her wild hot girl thoughts, hissing away the night.

'There's a party,' Jess says.

'Okay,' I say. She smiles at me with deranged crisp-crumbed teeth.

'We need to pick up for this,' she says.

Jess grew up around here so she has a local drug dealer's number. The first time I saw her pick up and get into the car and drive away, I ran after her, drunk, down the street, waving my arms and calling, 'Where are you taking her?' Then, terror-struck, I spent five minutes convincing myself she was kidnapped, tied up somewhere with jumper cables, my fingers hovering over 999 before she swung back round the corner, her red nails forking the breeze and Flo Rida blasting out onto the streetlight-pocked road.

This time I know what to do. We stand shivering on the street corner where the driver can slide in easily. We smoke cigarettes because there isn't anything else to do. Tiny silver arrows of rain dart down past the streetlight and we stand beneath it like we're standing in a sunbeam. Jess huddles into me, holding my arm with both of hers and leaning her dark spongey hair into my shoulder so I get a blast of fruit shampoo—orange or raspberry, I've never been good with scents. It makes me feel like a man even though when Jess is standing up normally she is half a foot taller than me. I try to solidify. I push my weight towards my feet, hoping she'll sense my stableness, and I clench my upper arms, hoping they'll feel less sloppy, and more like boys' arms, or at least the boys' arms I have liked in the mornings since I have started university, the kind that fit easily around my neck so that my head sort of rests on them, like a hat on a stand, or a watermelon the same size as the fruit bowl.

'Where is this fuckhead?' says Jess.

As if in answer, the drug dealer's car swings up and Jess leaps away from my shoulder and in two swift steps has ducked into the passenger side and he has driven away. Jess has explained that the drivers are paranoid about being picked up on the cameras so they must always circulate while the deal is struck. I have never seen the drivers up close but I have got flashes as Jess dips into the car, and she has described them to me. There is more than one driver but they are all Chinese, and they are not the man who answers the phone when Jess rings. No one knows who he is. The drivers are nice: one has a son and takes a long time showing Jess pictures; the others do not have sons but sometimes they talk about cars or the business of the night or traffic. One of them asked Jess for her number the first time we went out but she said no, even though after, when we had taken all the drugs and it was six am and we were in the park on our backs under the grey-streaked sky, she said she wished she had just done it because we could've got some free shit.

'And that,' she said, 'is the only reason to flirt!'

I shrugged. Normally I wouldn't have spoken but all that powder was forming unstoppable words in my throat.

'I don't know,' I said. 'What about getting people to like you?'

'Oh, sweets,' she said.

She put her arms around me but I was feeling uncomfortable so I just let her lie there, stretching over me. I started to hate myself so much for not being able to be normal and be hugged by a friend that I started to talk to explain, even though I wasn't even sure I had a good reason. It was most likely just my personality, that I wanted to be touched so badly and then didn't know how to be, that I tried so hard with the boys from the parties and their armpits but that I spent most of the time willing them to leave and that mostly I had to close my eyes and clench my fists when they were on top of me, that all sorts of horror flashed through my head, horror I couldn't even begin to start detailing because I deserved to be buried alive for thinking such things.

Normally I felt better bitching than talking but I was high for the first time and felt invincible with self-knowledge. I told Jess that the first time I got drunk I was fourteen and had just started at a new school, and we were all in the park on a Tuesday, one of those winter days when the lights switch off in the sky around four. We were drinking cider and it was sweet enough to drink quickly and I was going through a phase of feeling fat so I was only eating carrot sticks—anyway, what does it matter, it's just I was drunk because I didn't eat the sandwich that my mother had put in my bag.

Jess sat up and hugged her knees to her chest. I looked at her beneath all the lumpy grey clouds, and she looked beautiful and concerned, like the face you would see when you come out of a coma, except her pupils were penny-sized and she seemed to be chewing gum ferociously.

'Anyway,' I said, 'this girl who I did sunbeds with told me this boy liked me, and I was talking to him in the park, well, not really talking. He was a bit older. Anyway, when I went to pee in the bushes he followed me in, and it was really embarrassing because I'd just peed and my tights were all stuck round my ankles and I think I got a bit on my skirt and it smelt and was steaming in the cold. I really remember that, Jess, this little steamy path through my feet and I was trying to hide it, kind of crouch-dancing over it, but I was drunk so I don't know what it looked like I was doing. I thought he'd think I was really gross for peeing so then when he kissed me I was so pleased because I thought I'd managed to do something right.'

'Okay,' said Jess.

'Anyway, it was kind of hard to stay balanced and I fell over, and then he was on top of me, and I was lying in the pee and it really stank like cider, but I didn't want him to know that I'd peed, and he didn't seem to notice, and he was still kissing me and I hadn't kissed anyone so I didn't know what it was meant to be like, even though I didn't like it. Anyway, the only way I could cover the pee was if I lay down over it so I did.'

There was a bit of silence. It had started to rain in the park, and it smelt so pure and lovely, like water from some ancient fountain, and so different from the stinging shameful scent of the memory of my fourteen-year-old pee that I forgot my story. Jess lay back down next to me and put her head on my boobs, which squished a little sensitively beneath her. I tried to be boy-like and still like a hat stand or a fruit bowl and I patted her hair.

'Did he rape you?' she asked.

The rain tinkled down and for some reason it seemed funny to hear that word, the word I'd hidden because it was like a bomb you had to dance around, because even hearing the hint of its ticking would explode a whole horrible load of wreckage. And wreckage that wasn't inside anymore but outside for everyone to see and that you couldn't cover up with make-up or drinking or nice boys who wanted to know what your favourite tree was.

I said, 'Yeah, I guess.'

I left the 'I guess' there because I thought she could tell me that I guessed wrong and that him shoving himself into me while my own piss ran in a line down my spine wasn't anything unusual and shouldn't make me sad. I did lie down there, after all, my body doing the thing where it unknits itself and I freeze, freeze and don't kick or scream, although I did whisper, said *please stop*, which, after, I hated myself for doing because it meant I couldn't believe that I had wanted it the way everyone told me I had. It meant I hadn't wanted it, because I had asked him to stop, and worst was that I had said that tiny little desperate word, the word my mother always taught me to say like a nice little girl: *please*.

'That sucks,' said Jess, after a while. 'That shouldn't have happened to you, that's really fucking shitty.' She paused. 'I'd kill him if I could.'

My whole body felt alight in that moment. I imagined it must be like how when people believe in those miracle preachers and get touched on the head and fall over, flop, because I felt so relieved, in a way, and on fire with it, I'd never thought relief could be a burning feeling before, like love or shame or rage, but there it was, burning, just for a second. Then the second turned into another and the feeling was gone again.

Jess is taking ages. I'm nervous because the thing is I know one of the boys who lives in the house who is having the party tonight and he is not a nice boy. I met him at one of the nights during Freshers' Week. I went alone because I hadn't met Jess yet. There were only fifty people or so, most of us acne-scarred, craterous and lost as lonely white moons. We drifted around the dance floor, occasionally capturing the glance of a green strobe light that cast everyone in an alien hue, made the sillier of us look monstrous, which included me. I was wearing a white baby doll dress I'd got from a charity shop that may have been a child's nightie, but I thought it made me look somewhat attractive in a naïve way, with all my eyeliner and the song lyrics scrunched into tiny font on my trainers, penned in perfectionist straight lines with the help of an old protractor.

I ordered one of the fruit ciders you have over ice and it cost six pounds, which was half my budget for the night because my loan didn't cover my rent. I hadn't got a job yet, but I figured fuck it, thought maybe it made me look fancy, and it tasted good, like the colour pink slipping easily through my teeth. I hadn't eaten anything but toast since I'd moved two days ago and I hadn't spoken to anyone apart from the one girl I'd met on my floor who looked at me in my baby doll dress in such a horrified way I thought maybe she thought I was a ghost. I felt like a ghost so it didn't seem surprising to me. I finished off the whole ensemble with the leather jacket I got from Primark early last winter. I loved this jacket, loved the way it looked, the way it cut my waist in a thick way and the way my long dark hair blended in and caught the collar, the way the silver buckles near the neck flashed. So I felt like a ghost in a leather jacket and so I was invincible and invisible in the best way until the boy whose party it is tonight crashed into me. My pink strawberry cider blossomed across my boobs in the most clichéd of murder looks.

'Oh shit sorry, sorry, sorry,' he said, but it didn't sound the way sorry looks on a page—two distinct sounds, so and ree—he said it in a way that it all blended together like sweeeeeeee. I found it kind of funny, he looked like an actor on a TV show, but a funny TV show, playing drunk badly so you know it's pretend.

'It's okay,' I said. 'I was going to leave anyway.'

He looked me up and down and I looked at him looking me up and down. He had brown eyes but they looked all cracked up like when a mud puddle freezes over. It reminded me of jumping into those mud puddles and cracking them under my boots when I was child and this made me happy and trust him even though he hadn't done anything.

'You should stay,' he said. 'Do you want a drink?'

'Sure,' I said.

'Okay, can you get them? I'll be right back,' he said and walked off towards the toilets. The line stretched back onto the edge of the dance floor. I watched him join the line obediently. Then I wandered back up to the bar and replenished my pink drink and got him a beer. I zipped up my jacket over my boobs and felt pleasantly in control and strapped in like when they pull the guard down before the rollercoaster takes off. By the time he'd got back I'd finished my drink, so he got me another and we did a shot that came in a green plastic glass and tasted like apples. We said where we lived, what we were studying. We danced a little around each other, not touching at all. I was still feeling okay and when he put his hand on my back it felt good.

'Do you still want to go? I'll walk you to your stop, if you want,' he said.

'Okay, thanks,' I said. He didn't seem to be with anyone else and when we left he didn't say goodbye to anyone but by this time his hand was starting to feel weird on my back, because he didn't move it, just sort of manoeuvred me around to keep it there, and it started to feel less tender and more like his hand had got stuck there.

When we were outside I twisted away from him. My bus stop was behind the university and it was dark but not raining, just a dry dark cold. I guess he still wanted to touch me because he grabbed my neck while we were walking, this time with his thumb and one of his fingers, but it was hard and hurt and made me jerk my neck to the side and away but then he did it again, grabbed it. I thought of a nature documentary I saw once where they showed a man knee-deep in a swamp holding a baby alligator between two hands, how he had two fingers held like this boy's, this boy whose party it is tonight, and when he held the alligator's jaw in this way it had to open it, but it was frozen, its jaw locked and all its teeth, for all their scariness and sharpness, were useless and still in this man's enthusiastic grasp.

When we got to the bus stop I said very firmly and pleasantly, like I was talking to a child, 'I'm going home now, thanks for walking me.' I screwed my head from his grasp like a particularly hard lid pried free from the bottle.

I was just getting my phone out to see when the next bus was when he came up behind me and put his head on the right side of my neck. He breathed on me a bit. I moved away again but he pulled my right shoulder back towards him and kissed me. I pushed him away and sort of patted him in a way I thought was kind. I tried to raise the blue searching light of my phone between us but he grabbed my wrist and pushed his head underneath it until, in an odd turn of events, he was hunched over and I was the one who appeared to have him in a headlock, his hand still latched on hard to my wrist. He stuck his head back into my neck again and moved his mouth around. I wriggled a bit, but I couldn't move. It reminded me of playing a game with my father, one of my only memories of him, where he'd put his hand flat on my forehead and tell me to 'take a swing', and then laugh and laugh as my short arms flailed in the air between us, trying to please him as he pushed me to arm's length.

With his free hand the boy grabbed my right boob and gave it a rough, strange spin. I felt another rush of love for the jacket, that half-centimetre of leather like a bulletproof vest. He rubbed his palm around, his breath heavy with beer. I felt bile bobbing in my throat. I pushed my head to the side to avoid his breath and in a moment of clarity, I remembered an episode of Oprah I watched once with my mother. It was an educational episode on what to do if you were being raped. Oprah did an experiment in which an actress on the street, being dragged away by a man, yelled 'Help, I don't know this man! Help!' Everyone ignored her. I particularly remembered Oprah's serene and comforting face when she told everyone watching to always yell, 'FIRE' instead. When the rape actress yelled 'FIRE!', everyone looked at her with concern, as if they could at last see her flaming.

So I took a breath and shouted, 'FIRE', but my voice didn't come out, it was more of a strangled whisper, and none of the lights in any of the windows turned on but the boy did drop my boob and dip out from under my arm and say, 'What?'

I opened and closed my mouth.

He took a step back.

'You know, you just have to say if you don't like me,' he said.

'I don't like you,' I said, quickly.

He turned around and punched the plastic wall of the bus stop so the whole thing shuddered. I felt the tremor of it like it was happening within my own heart. Then he shouted much louder than I did and a light in the block of flats switched on above us. A shadow-head popped up like a puppet in the high yellow square. We both looked at it together, now politely side-by-side as though we had never touched.

'Fucking bitch,' he said, softly, before walking off into the dark. The yellow light stayed on in an angelic way, until I was on the bus. I stared at it as the bus wound down the road. As we turned the corner, it switched off like a breath being let go.

Jess spins back round the corner and triumphantly clambers out of the dealer's car. She holds my hand, the plastic packet between our palms like a sticker. We hide in the doorway of the real estate office. My stomach tightens like my intestines have gone in for an impressive handshake with each other. Jess seems fine. She does a couple of bumps with her house key and then hands it to me, and I copy her, two for two, and then she does another two and puts the keys in her pocket, pats it sweetly and then pats my head. 'Let's go,' she says.

I don't see who opens the door. Two rows of people in the hallway face each other, breathing furiously in and out of multi-coloured balloons. Jess sneaks her hand into mine and we wait a little awkwardly for the balloons to deflate. The hand Jess doesn't hold is starting to hurt, the handle of the plastic bag grooves into my skin, weighed down with its cans. The balloons shrink up. The blowers laugh maniacally, fall onto each other. The bus-stop boy is not in the hallway. The laughs drain out of all their faces as we watch.

'Let's go smoke,' says Jess. Her nails dig into my palm. The hallway is very narrow. We march through, pressed between bodies. On the stairs a girl is holding her phone to her ear and crying, eyeliner cracking and melting down her cheeks. She stares at us and bares her teeth. We push through the hallway. In the kitchen, another girl is perched on the counter, wearing a gold leotard, her hair gelled back and her ponytail so high as to be horizontal. She grips a boy between her bare legs and swings his head from side to side.

Another boy films them on his phone. The two boys are laughing but she is not. She looks at us, too. We walk past. The kitchen joins onto a living room, where maybe a dozen people are dancing. Four of them gyrate back and forth along each other, three girls behind a boy, the three girls dancing much more extravagantly. The boy looks a little crumpled by them, like he has gained an unwieldy hunchback. A few others swing around each other, their arms bound around necks and waists. 'I know you want it!' sings the song. 'I know you want it!' everyone goes. We walk through them with difficulty. Someone's hand strokes under my ass. I grip Jess's hand. There are big glass doors leading to the garden.

We open the doors and someone yells, 'Shut the door!' I shut the door behind me.

The garden is dark. From the light falling out of the living room I can make out some bins, a girl pushing a boy against the far fence on the other side of the overgrown grass. The grass is blackened in the dark. Delilah sits cross-legged in a patch of light. She is wearing a white baby doll dress. I am thrilled I threw mine swiftly away after the bus stop night. She hasn't got a coat on. Her arms and face are the same colour as the dress, but her black tights and ballet slippers blend into the black grass, so she looks as though she has grown straight out of the ground.

'Delilah!' says Jess, who immediately sits down beside her, throws an arm around her. I stand stupidly. I take a can out of the bag and it spits froth everywhere. I take a stroppy gulp. I don't understand why she is being nice to Delilah. We are the bitches! I remind her, telepathically. I am drunk, I remind myself, proudly.

'Don't be greedy,' says Jess. She takes her arm from around Delilah to take a can. I can't remember which one we are on. When do I stop remembering?

'You okay, Dee?' says Jess. 'You want a beer?'

Delilah looks at me. I slowly hand her one of the precious four we have left.

'Thanks,' she says.

'You okay?' says Jess. 'Listen, I'm sorry if I was kind of a bitch in that workshop today. I think your stuff is really good. Genuine. Like, you've actually been through shit, unlike all these idiots.'

When she says 'all these idiots', she waves her hand towards the house at large, me included. I take another long gulp of beer. The bumps have worn off. I can feel my lips scabbing.

The glass doors open again. The bus-stop boy comes out into the dark, holding a huge Sports Direct mug.

'Oh, woah, hey,' he says. He looks at Delilah. 'Introduce me, Didi!'

I fold my arms over my boobs, but the feel of my own arms on them makes me shake. Delilah makes a folded-up noise. Jess looks between us, then narrows her eyes at the boy.

'Whose this fuckhead?' she says. Some small part of me cheers.

Delilah is shaking in her silly white dress.

The boy smiles at Jess.

'Who are you?' he says.

Jess ignores him. She gets out the little white bag and does a key. I'm relieved when she hands it to me. Then she makes a key and hands it to Delilah who stares at her, terrified. Jess takes it.

'Got one of those for me?' says the boy.

'No,' says Jess.

'Why?' His voice tightens up a little. 'What, you don't like me? How come? You been saying something?'

He looks at Delilah, who stares at her white lap. Jess raises up one of her taloned hands and wriggles her fingers at him as though to dismiss him. He looks between Delilah and Jess and then turns to me. I raise my beer can to my face hoping the bottom eclipses it, not wanting him to recognise me, not wanting him to tell Jess. I wish I'd never told her anything. I wish I never said any words ever. Someone starts playing the same song again. The can's empty. I have to put it down to get another.

'Hey, I recognise you,' says the bus-stop boy, and smiles. He puts a hand on my arm, as if to turn me a little more towards him, not hard. I raise my eyebrows hard and try to make an apathetic face, biting both rows of my teeth together. I try to separate myself from my body, imagine myself quickly as someone else. Jess? She is staring at us, her eyes narrowed. Delilah? She is saying something in Jess's ear. The dancers in the living room? Are they happy? Are they winning? Is anyone? The girl pushes the boy against the fence with another slam. I don't want to be anyone. I feel the fingers of bus-stop boy on my arm. I think how underneath our skins we are all ridiculous-looking skeletons, just bony jokes. I'd like to be bone. Would I like to be dead? Not in a morose way, just for the peace. I'd like to sleep. I'd like to be held and not be horrified. Maybe that happens when you're dead.

'Just let me liberate you!' sings the man in the song.

Jess stands up and carefully takes the bus-stop boy's hand off my arm. She holds it in hers. She is at least three inches taller than him. Her nails stick out between his fingers like claws.

'Let's dance,' she says, and marches him off into the living room.

'Shut the door!' the room yells.

The door is shut.

I sit down beside Delilah and start to roll a cigarette. Her head is still lowered.

'I'd never kissed a boy before,' she whispers.

I think of the wedding dresses. I don't know what to say. I can't hug her and I don't want to tell her I'm the same because I don't want to be the same as Delilah. But I take her hand. I feel it tense up so I stop holding it, give no pressure at all, just let my hand flop on hers. I give it a little stroke. With my free hand I take a long slug of beer, ready to stop remembering.

'Look,' says Delilah.

I look up. The air has tightened with silence, and I realise someone has stopped playing the song at last. In the living room, the dancers are clearing the floor. Two people crouch on the armchair as if they have just leaped there. One boy is flattening himself further against the wall. In the centre, Jess and the bus-stop boy are circling each other slowly, the circles getting wider as the dancers give them room.

'What are they doing?' Delilah asks. 'Are they dancing?'

An image of the future blows out before me then. Delilah, married, teaching, will win a poetry prize in her sixties. The cover will have a raven with a rose stem in its mouth. I will give up writing completely, fall into a job writing copy for a weekly vegetable box delivery service, admired for my produce-based puns. I'll end up with someone nice, and I'll betray them carefully with someone horrible. At the end of my life I'll curl up like a dried leaf and blow away, leaving no trace, and this will be a comfort.

And Jess?

Jess stops circling. She holds up three fingers, folds one down, then another. The bus-stop boy laughs, looks around the room, but no one else is laughing. Jess folds down the last finger, then immediately darts in at the boy with one arm raised as if to punch him. The boy ducks under her fast, spins back and catches her round the waist. He bends her over, gets her in a headlock. Delilah lets out a little gasp. The boy is still laughing, looking around the room as if to find someone to give the laugh to. Jess flails her arms madly upwards like tentacles. The boy stops laughing, his face tightening as he tries to keep his balance, hold her still. Slaps and breaths travel muffled through the window. The crowd around are blank-faced, staring. One girl silently holds up a phone.

Jess kicks her feet back and with her right foot she manages to crack one of the boy's knees. It sounds wonderful, the crack. It slides right through the glass to us. His mouth buds upwards, and he must soften his grip because Jess pulls his arm off her neck and throws him off with such force that he spins away. He lands against the counter that separates the living room from the kitchen, gripping it with both knuckles. She marches over behind him before he has a chance to get away, grabs him by his right shoulder and flips him over to face her like she's opening a book. Then she puts both of her hands on his shoulders, pushing him down firmly. He wriggles a little, and then she lifts him up by both shoulders before throwing his whole weight back against the counter, where his head clips the edge. He slithers down to the floor, his eyes still open. I look for blood but none arrives. Still, he stops trying to move. He watches her like the rest of us. Like she has become inevitable, which is what I have always known. She kneels down over him, locking his arms to his sides with her long legs. Then she raises one arm towards the ceiling, her red nails catching the light as she lowers one perfect scalloped point towards the boy's eyeball.

Beside me, Delilah makes a sound, like a breath is being torn out of her. I think she is crying, and I'm about to force myself to hug her, but when I turn to look at her, she is grinning, shaking with laughter, the kind of laughter that is so hard it hurts. Looking at her makes me start too. I feel the laugh brew in my stomach, stretch my lungs apart and skip up my throat. I stop watching the fight. I throw my head back to the empty-starred sky instead, take a breath to prepare. The cackle that comes is as long as a howl, as sharp as a scream.

Waves

[Read once forward, once backwards, quite fast.]

slipped on
each breaks
final adverb
can we differ
almost Sappho
did she leap
a roar apiece
each a span
no attention
pearls & condoms
say shuddering
bottom sand
nerves to ply
shock to manage
no 'others'
no 'cost'
quit dreaming
drive for shore
don't go loose
I meant terms
no terms
softly lift
tone murderous
manic friend
ungraspable
who could
('cried Gilbert…')
swim you
pale sky
('… beautifully…')
ever on, ever on

Anne Carson

from Capriccio

As a child she was taught to classify at the breakfast table.

A leak in the calendar.

No concert in the gallery.

We bond over pastis and an unwavering belief in the gesture of unveiling.

One day goes undiagnosed, then the next.

She said she wanted to compile an index of the present.

A platter of stubby candles dipped in toffee cream.

Is there any ending that isn't trivial?

No collective hydro scheme.

*

A countess spends an afternoon choosing between her two suitors, Music and Poetry.

A single slide on the Palladian powerpoint.

#bumwine

First the music and then the words.

I invent an instrument for gauging suspense in psychological thrillers.

Animals in a revolving door.

Do I desire to escape my body or to understand how to patch it.

I was curious about territory so I pissed by the footpath.

*

At this point, some directors bring down a curtain and there is an interval.

She orders hot cocoa in the drawing room.

A wagtail on the gable rake.

A season buckled with potential.

Choppy air, and an epicurean confusion of how with why.

I howl at my sentences and they chafe at an upper limit.

A bird, and other wind instruments.

*

I was told to sleep with my heart elevated, to let the futurity drain.

How often a path is just gravity, and then some.

I've made peace with rocky perception.

Green rays for all your oceans.

In the midst of familial fog I pick pinecones to anticipate an occasion.

If you think a tree lacks imagination, take a look at a self.

A garment promoted to a raiment.

Somewhere, an architecture quickens.

*

poem continues

Or, every log is a backlog.

They burned the lyric to force its renewal.

A brief interlude on someone else's channel.

Your step in the forest synonymous with tripwire, some zoic cadence screeching *intruder*.

That sweet aroma is a distress signal.

If you don't know this by now.

A garden is a tree zoo.

Dalmatian hobble.

No additional text.

*

Was a pronoun always an aide memoire.

I—Monsieur Taupe—am the prompter, the most important component.

Ode to the windswept husband.

Posture like a cypress.

Outside animals annul.

Inside animals enamel.

The wind comes apart in sedimentary flakes.

Birdfall.

I forget my lines.

*

A hop-skip-jump of recollection.

Will unanchored non-sequential utterance exhaust expression or will it pique.

My glittering career at the egg-and-spoon relay.

Anyone could become accustomed to being waited on.

A blank page misattributed.

The contents of a house splayed out on the lawn, clover deep.

Sheela na gig, my feminine touch.

Every door opened is a wound, dehisced.

*

A menagerie of imitation snacks on itself.

Why We Miss the Pre-Agricultural Matriarchy.

Clickbait fanning an aura.

A raven shares my problem.

A hot mustang carouses.

A maenad becomes overwhelmed by her rod of giant fennel.

*

What we unlearned in 2013.

A dish of blue lichen appeals.

To irk an exhibitionist.

Invoices I have been.

Daisy Lafarge

A Short Story But It's Written Like An Internet Meme

Hayley Carr

The bus doors concertina open and I step out into the brisk, autumnal air, crisp as lettuce and smokey as smoked cheese. The sky is empty of clouds, leaving behind a bare, blue skin through which the cold permeates. The air hardens around the exposed flesh of my hands and face, and as I walk down the cracked and gum-mottled pathway I have the sense of turning into an ice sculpture.

When I pass the Four Courts, I see a couple huddled together inside a sleeping bag, like children hiding from morning. The woman sits up and pops her red face out of the covers to yell something to another duvet mound, cocooned on the opposite platform of the entrance a few metres away. The mound is unresponsive and possibly dead, and the woman sighs, and retreats into her faded blue-striped sleeping bag. I keep my head low, not knowing where to look, feeling so out of touch. When there are no cars, I cross the road and gingerly pass the tree with all the used up syringes. The syringes make me feel nervous, despite their familiarity, as predictable now as the brown, discarded leaves crunching under my shoes.

The billboard off Usher's Quay has changed since yesterday. Despite my complete lack of interest in Halloween-themed soft drinks, I stare at it gawk-eyed as I cross the bridge, trying to read all the information before I reach the other side. Even crossing the lights I crane my head distractedly towards the giant black and orange poster, like a lemming spontaneously drawn to a cliff edge. A car beeps abruptly and I jolt, clasping my hands instinctually to my chest. I turn in the direction of the sound and an irate-looking driver is glaring at me through the windscreen of his car, making an exasperated gesture with his hands, telling me to cross already. I raise an apologetic hand and smile meekly before I jog clumsy-footed across the rest of the road.

I feel a sinking sense of stupidity, a lead curtain weight clinging heavily to my stomach. Embarrassment pours through my face in a vivid red blush. But no one notices me; they just walk by, heads bowed, on their phones, or their eyes distant and dreamy, thinking of their own stupidities and embarrassments.

When I reach my office, the feeling has dissipated, somewhat. I root around in my pocket for the door fob, extracting it from my nest of keys, which snag on the lip of my pocket as I pull them out. A middle-aged man wearing a tattered baseball cap watches me skeptically from the curb, sucking on a cigarette and exhaling smoke as if it were some charm that could protect him from me. I'm about to press the candy-corn shaped fob against the receiver, when I realise both office doors are already wide open. A voice calls from within the building, and the man breaks his gaze, flicking the stub of his cigarette to the pavement.

I stoop through the doors unnecessarily, feeling dwarfed by their spacious aperture. The security guard is sitting at his desk, as per usual, dragging his eyes from his laptop to me like a mouse cursor. I smile and offer a feeble 'hi' in a pitch at least an octave higher than my usual voice. Before he can instigate another one of his intense morning conversations, I swiftly attempt to climb the stairs, but when I hop up the first few steps, two men and a large filing cabinet appear at the top. The men are attempting to carry the large filing cabinet down the stairs. I dishearteningly plod down the few steps, backing up to the security guard's desk to give them space, prey stumbling straight into the lion's den.

He watches me with an almost menacing focus. There's an anticipatory smile on his face, as though he's observing someone opening a gift he's given them. In return, I offer a polite, nervous smile, like someone who's just received a semi-automatic weapon for their birthday when all they asked for was a Barbie doll.

'Has anyone ever told you you look like Daphne from *Scooby-Doo*? Do you ever get that?'

I look at him. 'Do you mean Velma?' I reply, considering my short brown hair, small stature, and the fact that I can't see without my glasses.

'Velma, sorry. Do you get that, do you?'

'No,' I wilt, 'no one's ever said that to me.'

'Oh really?'

'Really.'

'Take it as a compliment. She was the smart one.'

'Yeah,' I say, tentatively watching the two men in their struggle to lug the cabinet down the stairs. The side of it has now gotten stuck against the lower ceiling, and they're attempting to manoeuvre it past.

'As far as I remember they had the smart one, the dumb one, the dog one, and the handsome one. Isn't that right?'

'Yeah,' I confirm, wondering if 'the dog one' is really a TV archetype.

'And wasn't Shaggy supposed to be a stoner or something? And when he got hungry he actually had the munchies.'

'Yeah.'

'I always remember they had the big sandwiches.'

'Yeah.'

'And that's implying that they had been smoking.'

'Presumably, yeah,' I say. Then, more alert: 'Well, the dog, he wasn't on drugs.'

'Probably was on drugs,' he says darkly, as if the Mystery Gang were some group of sordid, depraved scumbags. 'How old were they, were they kids or were they adults?'

'They were teenagers.'

The two men lumber past me out the wide-open doors with the cumbersome cabinet in their arms, and I wonder how I got drawn into this conversation. Ooh, how I envy that cabinet.

'I can't remember, all I remember is—I thought they were in their early twenties, or were they, like, in their late teens or something?'

God help me.

'I think they were meant to be, like, late teens,' I say, becoming frustrated, because everyone knows they were a bunch of meddling kids.

'Or maybe their early twenties at most.'

'Yeah.' No. Somewhere outside a car alarm goes off, honking in the background like a seagull. 'I'd say, like, between sixteen and eighteen, to be honest. That's what I think.'

'I mean, they're driving, so presumably they're about seventeen, eighteen.'

'You can drive at sixteen in America.'

'I suppose so, yeah. But I assume they're out of high school.'

I don't know why this guy is so fixated on establishing the lore of a sixties cartoon. I try to look enthusiastic, nodding as he speaks, maintaining eye contact, but when that becomes too much of a challenge, I try my best to at least temper my bored, exasperated expression, surreptitiously making my way over to the staircase, with the imperceptible progress of a snail.

'I don't really think that logic was too important to the show,' I say, laughing anaemically while I mount the first step.

'I don't know. The smart ones—if they're still in high school they'd all be going to school or whatever.'

I try to think of an episode of *Scooby-Doo* in which the gang just attends lessons all day, and tries to solve the mystery of the tricky algebra equation. It doesn't seem as interesting.

'I don't know,' I offer feebly, ascending another stair.

'I don't know. I don't remember. All I remember is bits and pieces of *Scooby-Doo* as a child. And *Scooby Dooby Doo*!' He imitates the line with a self-satisfied grin, as if this were one of his party tricks and he is dying to impress me. I stare at him with what I hope is amusement, but is more likely a cross between fear and discomfort.

'*Scooby Dooby Doo*!' he roars again with even more enthusiasm, as though I hadn't fully appreciated the genius of his impression the first time round. I chuckle awkwardly, taking the opportunity to climb up two more steps. If this were an episode of *Scooby-Doo* he would definitely end up being the guy in the costume at the end, dressing up as some campy monster to scare off the addicts of Merchants Quay. There is a lingering silence, and I fidget with my fingers, my eyes twitching longingly towards the top of the staircase, trying to determine whether the conversation has finally reached its natural conclusion.

I begin to mutter a goodbye and then realise that I haven't thought of anything to say, so I'm just flapping my mouth soundlessly as I sidestep up the stairs.

'Do you like James Bond?' he asks when I'm on the first landing, beside the men's toilets.

I feel the air in my body collapse like a deflated pastry. 'No,' I say, hoping he can detect the note of queasiness in my voice.

'There's this fan theory on the internet that James Bond is actually just a code name, so it's not supposed to be the same James Bond each time...' He cranes his neck upward to look at me from the floor below. I don't even try to look interested anymore, I simply listen with growing dejection as he describes in further detail the intricacies of the theory, and I fear I'll be trapped in this spot for the remainder of my life.

Just then one of my colleagues walks through the two wide-open doors, observing them with an air of mild curiosity, before nodding curtly at the security guard and jogging up the stairs.

'Hi!' I exclaim far more jubilantly than is warranted. My colleague regards my beaming face with uncertainty before his features morph into a look of understanding, half sympathetic, half amused.

'Hiya, Hayley,' he says as casually as possible, and then plods past me up the stairs.

'Well, I better go,' I say to the security guard, and I walk obligingly behind my colleague like an adoring puppy. I don't even wait for the guard to say anything before I go, giggling internally with joyous relief, running now up the stairs and down the corridor to my office as quickly and as subtly as possible before another endless conversation can be struck up. With my colleague beside me, I input the door code and pull down on the handle, pushing open the office door with mortal haste.

'Do you like *Scooby-Doo*?'

The security guard is sitting at his desk as per usual, glaring at me through the windscreen of his car. I feel the air in my body collapse like a deflated pastry.

'Yeah,' I say feebly, as embarrassment pours through my face in a vivid red blush.

'Oh really?'

'No.'

'There's this fan theory on the internet that the Mystery Gang were actually a group of sordid, depraved scumbags.'

'You can drive at sixteen in America,' I say, alert. There is an exasperated silence, and I fidget with my fingers, my eyes twitching longingly towards the couple cocooning under the security guard's desk, trying to determine whether the mystery of the tricky algebra equation has finally been solved.

'Were they kids or were they addicts?' he asks abruptly, in a pitch at least an octave higher than his usual voice. Somewhere outside a seagull goes off, honking in the background like a car alarm. Surreptitiously, I make my way down two steps, with the imperceptible progress of a lion.

'I don't know,' I offer feebly.

'Shaggy was supposed to be a stoner, and when he got hungry he actually had the munchies.'

'You can drive at sixteen in America.'

'I always remember they had semi-automatic weapons, and that's implying they had been smoking.' He flicks the stub of his cigarette to the cracked and gum-mottled pavement. I try to look enthusiastic, but my expression is more likely a cross between fear and discomfort.

'Has anyone ever told you you look like a Barbie doll? Do you ever get that?'

I look at him. 'Do you mean God?' I reply, considering my short brown hair, giant stature, and the fact that I know all.

'God, sorry. Do you get that, do you?'

'Yeah.' I plod down the few steps, like a lemming drawn to a cliff edge, backing up to the security guard's desk.

'Take it as a compliment. He was the dog one.'

'Yeah,' I confirm, wondering if he likes James Bond.

'All I remember are bits and pieces as a child,' he says darkly.

'Well, I better go,' I say to the security guard, while I walk obligingly through the bus doors, out into the brisk autumnal air, crisp as smoked cheese, smokey as lettuce. The sky is empty of seagulls, leaving behind a bare, blue skin through which the conversation permeates. The air hardens around the exposed flesh of my hands and face, and as I walk down the cracked and gum-mottled corridor, I see two men attempting to carry a large filing cabinet down the stairs. I dishearteningly cross the road and gingerly pass the tree with all the used-up algebra equations. The equations amuse me, despite their discomfort, now as predictable as the brown, discarded syringes crunching under my shoes.

The side of the cabinet has now gotten stuck against the lower ceiling, and I stare at the two men gawk-eyed as I cross the bridge, as they try to manoeuvre it past, despite my complete lack of interest in men and cabinets. Even crossing the lights I crane my head distractedly towards the giant black and orange men, like a man spontaneously drawn to a cabinet. A Halloween-themed seagull honks abruptly and I jolt, hopping up the first few steps of the stairs instinctually. I turn in the direction of the sound, and a middle-aged man wearing a tattered sandwich on his head watches me skeptically, sucking on candy corn as if it were real corn. I raise an apologetic hand, thinking if this were an episode of *Scooby-Doo* he would definitely end up being the guy in the costume at the end, dressing up as some stoner teenager to scare off the campy couples of Merchants Quay.

I stoop through the wide-open office doors unnecessarily, feeling dwarfed by their small stature. The security guard is huddled under a sleeping bag, like a dead body, dragging his eyes from the lion to me like a mouse cursor. I smile and offer a feeble 'goodbye' in a pitch at least an octave lower than my usual voice. I swiftly attempt to climb the stairs before he can instigate an algebra lesson, but when I hop up the first few steps I see a couple attempting to touch each other jubilantly, their flesh exposed. I obligingly plod down the few steps, backing up to the security guard's cabinet to give them space, like children walking straight into an irate driver's car.

He watches me with an almost sordid look, a cheesy smile on his face, as though fingering someone's exposed flesh. I return his grin with a curt, queasy smile, like someone who's just received a Barbie doll for their birthday when all they asked for was a semi-automatic weapon.

'And that's implying that they had been smoking.'

I look at him. 'And wasn't Shaggy supposed to be a stoner or something?' I reply, considering my short brown hair, small stature, and the fact that I can't see without my glasses. 'And when he got hungry he actually had the munchies.'

'As far as I remember they had the smart one, the dumb one, the dog one, and the handsome one. Isn't that right?'

'Do you like James Bond?' I wilt. 'Do you mean Velma?'

'Has anyone ever told you you look like Daphne from *Scooby-Doo*? Do you ever get that?'

'Hi!'

'Hiya, Hayley.'

'How old were they, were they kids or were they adults?' I say, tentatively watching the two men in their struggle to lug the cabinet down the stairs. The side of it has now gotten stuck against the lower ceiling, and they're attempting to manoeuvre it past.

'I always remember they had the big sandwiches.'

'I can't remember, all I remember is—I thought they were in their early twenties, or were they, like, in their late teens or something?' I confirm, wondering if 'the dog one' is really a TV archetype.

'I don't know'

'I don't know. I don't remember. All I remember is bits and pieces of *Scooby-Doo* as a child. And *Scooby Dooby Doo!*'

'I don't know. The smart ones—if they're still in high school they'd all be going to school or whatever.'

'I don't really think that logic was too important to the show.'

'I'd say, like, between sixteen and eighteen, to be honest. That's what I think.'

'I mean, they're driving, so presumably they're about seventeen, eighteen,' I say. Then, more alert, say, 'I suppose so, yeah. But I assume they're out of high school.'

'I think they were meant to be, like, late teens,' he says darkly, as if the Mystery Gang were some group of sordid, depraved scumbags. 'No.'

'No.' The two men lumber past me with the cumbersome cabinet in their arms, and I wonder how I got drawn into this conversation. Ooh, how I envy that cabinet.

'No one's ever said that to me.'

God help me.

'Oh really?' I say, becoming frustrated, because everyone knows they were a bunch of meddling kids.

'Or maybe their early twenties at most.'

'Presumably, yeah.' No. Somewhere outside a car alarm goes off, honking in the background like a seagull. 'Probably was on drugs.'

'Really.'

'*Scooby Dooby Doo!*'

'Take it as a compliment. She was the smart one.' I don't know why this guy is so fixated on establishing the lore of a sixties cartoon. I try to look enthusiastic, nodding as he speaks, maintaining eye contact, but when that becomes too much of a challenge, I try my best to at least temper my bored, exasperated expression, surreptitiously making my way over to the staircase, with the imperceptible progress of a snail.

'There's this fan theory on the internet that James Bond is actually just a code name, so it's not supposed to be the same James Bond each time...' I say, laughing anaemically while I mount the first step.

'They were teenagers.'

I try to think of an episode of *Scooby-Doo* in which the gang just attends lessons all day, and tries to solve the mystery of the tricky algebra equation. It doesn't seem as interesting.

'Velma, sorry. Do you get that, do you?' I offer feebly, ascending another stair.

'Well, I better go.' He imitates the line with a self-satisfied grin, as if this were one of his party tricks and he is dying to impress me. I stare at him with what I hope is amusement, but is more likely a cross between fear and discomfort.

'Well, the dog, he wasn't on drugs,' he roars again with even more enthusiasm, as though I hadn't fully appreciated the genius of his impression the first time round. I chuckle awkwardly, taking the opportunity to climb up two more steps, thinking if this were an episode of *Scooby-Doo* he would definitely end up being the guy in the costume at the end, dressing up as some campy monster to scare off the addicts of Merchants Quay. There is a lingering silence, and I fidget with my fingers, my eyes twitching longingly towards the top of the staircase, trying to determine whether the conversation has finally reached its natural conclusion.

I begin to mutter a goodbye and then realise that I haven't thought of anything to say, so I'm just flapping my mouth soundlessly as I sidestep up the stairs.

'Yeah?' he asks abruptly, and I feel the air in my body collapse like a deflated pastry.

'Yeah,' I say, already at the men's toilets on the first landing, hoping he can detect the note of queasiness in my voice.

'Yeah,' he begins to explain, craning his neck upward to look at me from the floor below. I don't even try to look interested anymore, I simply listen with growing dejection as he describes in further detail the intricacies of the theory, fearing that I'll be trapped in this spot for the remainder of my life.

Just then one of my colleagues walks through the two wide-open doors, observing them with an air of mild curiosity before nodding curtly at the security guard and jogging up the stairs.

'Yeah,' I exclaim far more jubilantly than is warranted. My colleague regards my beaming face with some uncertainty before his features morph into a look of understanding, half sympathetic, half amused.

'Yeah,' he says as casually as possible, before plodding past me up the stairs.

'You can drive at sixteen in America,' I say to the security guard, walking feebly behind my colleague like an anaemic lemming. I don't even wait for him to solve the case of the mystery of the brown leaves, because everyone knows they turn brown in autumn. I giggle internally with menacing sympathy, running [*around robbing banks, all whacked off of Scooby Snacks*] up the stairs and down the corridor to my office as quickly and as awkwardly as possible before another guy in a costume appears to suck on my exposed flesh. With my colleague beside me, like an obliging puppy, I input the door code and pull down on the handle, pushing open the office door with mortal haste. I step into the Halloween-themed office. The security guard is dressed in a lion costume, as per usual, observing the couple huddled under my desk with an air of mild curiosity, becoming hard. Probably on drugs. I make my way over to my desk, as I root around in my pocket for candy corn, extracting a small concertina dishearteningly, as embarrassment pours through my face in a vivid red blush. I smile and offer a feeble honk of my concertina, but no one notices me; they just look on, their eyes distant and dreamy, thinking of their own concertinas.

I swiftly attempt to climb the stairs before the security guard can appreciate my concertina, but when I hop up the first few steps I see two dwarfs attempting to carry a large, human-shaped mound down the stairs. I stare gawk-eyed at the two men as they struggle to lug the dead body, making an exasperated gesture with my hand telling them to go already.

'Are you on drugs?' the security guard asks casually. I surreptitiously watch the couple, cocooning in the cabinet opposite, eat the dead body.

'Probably, yeah,' I say.

'You have the munchies?' he asks as I eat a sandwich with lettuce and cheese. It's like the sky, but not blue.

'Yeah.'

'Take it as a compliment.'

'No,' I say, head full of clouds. He regards my bored face with some uncertainty before his features morph into a look of understanding, half nervous, half amused.

'Has anyone ever told you you look like the soft-drink bottle from the billboard? Do you get that?'

'Are you on drugs?' I ask, more alert.

'I don't remember.'

'All I remember is I'm the dog one.' I stare at him with growing dejection, feeling the air in my body collapse like a crunched snail, fearing that I'll be trapped in this dog body for the remainder of my life.

'Take it as a compliment.'

'I used to be God,' I say, in a pitch at least an octave higher than the men's toilets. He cranes his neck upward to look at me from his den below, his eyes distant and dreamy, thinking about campy men.

'There's this fan theory on the internet that God is actually just a code name for Dog,' he begins to explain enthusiastically. I don't even try to temper my bored, frustrated expression, making an exasperated gesture with my hand telling him to go already. He looks at me longingly like an adoring puppy and I chuckle awkwardly, taking the opportunity to smoke some more drugs, thinking if this were an episode of *Scooby-Doo* everyone would be running around, robbing banks, all whacked off of Scooby Snacks.

'Do you like—'

'Well, I better go,' I say abruptly, swiftly retreating down the stairs and out the wide-open office doors into the brisk, autumnal air. The sky is empty of clouds, leaving behind a bare, blue skin through which the cold permeates. The air hardens around the exposed flesh of my hands and face, and I have the sense of turning into a campy *Scooby-Doo* monster. A middle-aged man with ginger hair and a Barbie doll in his hand watches me with a menacing focus, his eyes observing me as I walk down the cracked and gum-mottled pathway. I back up to the man abruptly.

'What?'

'You look like a witch,' he says, and I consider my black nest of hair, my Halloween-themed costume, and the obliging familiar sitting at my foot.

'I'm dressed up,' I offer feebly.

'You're a witch!' the man roars, his expression a cross between fear and amusement.

'I think she looks more like Daphne from *Scooby-Doo*,' the security guard says. I jolt, clasping my hands instinctually to my chest.

'Velma,' I say abruptly. '*He* looks like Daphne.' I gesture at the man with the ginger hair.

'Velma, sorry. Do you get that, do you?' The man starts honking his concertina, as if it were a charm that could protect him from me.

'No,' I say, becoming frustrated. 'No one's ever said that to me.'

'Oh, really?'

'Really really.'

'Take it as a compliment. She was the one who could morph into a filing cabinet.'

'Because she was a witch!' the man says. I sigh irritably, thinking that this conversation has become very stupid, fearing that I'll be trapped in this spot for the remainder of my life. Just then one of my colleagues walks down the pavement toward us, nodding curtly at the two men.

'Hi!' I exclaim far more jubilantly than is warranted. My colleague regards my beaming face with some uncertainty before his features morph into a look of understanding, half sympathetic, half amused.

'Hiya Hayley,' he says as casually as possible, before walking through the two wide-open doors, observing them with an air of mild curiosity.

'Well, I better go,' I say to the security guard.

'Has anyone ever—'

'I better go.'

'Do you like—'

'Goodbye!' I walk obligingly after my colleague like an adoring puppy, stooping through the doors unnecessarily, feeling dwarfed by their spacious aperture. The security guard is sitting at his desk, as per usual, dragging his eyes from his laptop to me like a mouse cursor. I smile and offer a feeble 'hi', my eyes twitching longingly towards the top of the staircase, but my colleague is already at the men's toilets.

'*Scooby Dooby Doo!*' the security guard roars.

'What?'

'Because you look like the girl from *Scooby-Doo*. Do you get that, do you?'

I sigh.

'Occasionally,' I say. 'Occasionally.'

Because I finished something, I thought
I could begin again. It's more a strange intervention
of personality that settles on an ending than anything else.
When I was younger—maybe you, too—the immediate
response would have been inadvertently offensive
but I've made a point of exceeding my own expectations.
Wildflowers Out of Gas
by Joe Ceravolo: Corina gave this to me oh like eight years ago.
It was a photocopy, but it was her only copy. I think
Mac had made it for her? He, I know, is a zealot
for Ceravolo, once held Joe's then-unpublished long poem,
The Hellgate, to a xerox machine and couldn't go through with it
or was otherwise caught. I suspect the latter. He may have gotten
a page or two. Computers invading the penis and breast or cleaning
them away. It's one or the other. Joe's god clears the system
or complicates it, a poem of the holy body, carnal revisions
to divinity, dedicated to divinity itself. A friend
tweets their mother has passed away, and the mentions
start trending. I see them all day but don't reply.

[*Brooklyn, 12-12-18*]

Ted Dodson

I Am Andrew Wyeth!
David Means

If I remember correctly—and I believe I do—I asked Christina to bring the agreement with her to Grand Central Station for an initial meeting about a week before Christmas. Arrive with it signed, if you don't mind, I told her over the phone. We found a table in the food court on the lower level and sat down together, and I explained right away that my reasoning behind having her sign the agreement wasn't so much about my being secretive, or wanting to hide behind a legal document, but really because the document would allow me to maintain—I believe I said—an appearance of intentional isolation. Thanks to the agreement, I could share my thoughts with her without resorting to self-editing—I believe I used that exact phrase, *self-editing*—and then she smiled slightly as I went on to explain that I wasn't a secretive person. I'm not a soul inclined to withhold, I said. As a matter of fact, I'm the kind of person who feels compelled to make confessions, and perhaps by having you sign this piece of paper I'm building a structure in which my secrets can be kept externally, outside my own mind, so, for example, if I start to tell you about my family, meaning my sisters and my parents, I'll do so knowing that my words, while being heard, will also be reaching a safe, terminal home. Whereas if you refused to sign that agreement, I said, pointing to the contract in her hands, I might feel compelled to begin confessing this and that anyway, partly out of a sense that you're a good listener, and I can tell you are by the way you touch your ear now and then, adjusting your hair away from your cheeks (she had a habit of taking a strand or two of her long, auburn hair and tweezing, tweezing, and then carefully, with deliberateness that I found absurdly charming, placing it behind her ear, which was small, shell-like, and delicate.). If you don't sign the contract, I'll view you as a conduit to the outside world. Because that's the way I work. I mean I've had a habit in the past of talking to people—usually untrustworthy people—with an awareness that, for example, when I tell them that my father was a bad drunk, and that he fell down the stairs one winter afternoon when I was fifteen and broke three ribs, and that I was the one who dialled for the police, they'll take that information, share it with others, embellishing, bending my words into their own (his father was a junkie, and fell down the stairs and broke six ribs), and then pass it on to someone who will do the same until the story I originally told no longer relates to *my* past but to the past of several imaginary people, floating around out there as a story about *my* father.

I told her this, and, as a way of giving another example, told her about the time my sister stole a cheque out of a mailbox. I described the mailbox, one of those apartment mailboxes with the little slot for the name and address, with a useless, small cellophane window, and a key that only the mailman was supposed to have, along, perhaps, with the building super, and how he opened up a long row of boxes all at once. I explained how my sister stole the key from the super's office, or, perhaps she got there when the mailman arrived and grabbed it when he wasn't looking (I wasn't sure, I added) and then very carefully took the cheque back to her room at the halfway house and forged a signature. It was a government child support cheque for five hundred dollars, and she cashed it at the bank down the street from her halfway house, not far from the Michigan state capitol building. What's important, I believe I told Christina, is that one wouldn't think my sister would have the skill to pull it off, not only to forge the signature but also to take it to a teller and persuade her, or him, to cash it without the proper identification. Anyway, I believe I said, You see, if we didn't have the non-disclosure agreement I'd tell you this story and then you'd tell someone else, and I trust you'd stick mostly to the facts because you seem like the trustworthy type, but *they* wouldn't stick to the facts. To add some zest to my original version, they'd say my sister stole a thousand dollars. They'd say she was a kind of idiot savant, brilliant at forgery, able to replicate just about any kind of document, and then someone else, passing it on, would make it a mailbox at the house of some renowned Michigan personage, a state senator, perhaps, and they'd describe how she snuck up to the front door on a clear, cool fall day, or perhaps they'd even make it in my hometown instead of Lansing, because they'd know at least that fact about my past, and they'd be telling it with a relish that comes from passing an inside bit of gossip about a reclusive artist, one who has been obsessively panting scenes of the Pennsylvania countryside for the last fifteen years.

In the past—I explained to Christina—my mouth was a conduit for the flow of information outward. In the past I told personal anecdotes that were carefully shaped to allow for the future filling in, or, rather, fictionalisation, by souls who didn't know me. I took into account the way a bit of narrative might get passed from a close friend, a kind-hearted person with the best intentions, to someone removed from me who would take the story and turn it against me, so that somehow I would be implicated in the story. For example, a mean-hearted person might say that I was the one who taught my sister how to forge a decent cheque, and how to persuade a teller to cash the cheque. (I did teach her how to forge a cheque, and I did talk to her about the nature of teller work and how to be usefully confusing in a transaction at the counter, but that's beside the point.)

Then we were on our second coffee and she explained (in a voice that I now see was slightly too firm, too officious, I think) that she would be delighted to be my assistant, and that whatever I said—and she said this, I swear—would stay *in her mind*, and in her mind only, from that moment on, for the rest of time itself (she said that: *the rest of time*) and then she seemed to blush, touched her ear again and ever so gently lifted her cup and sipped in what seems to me now, looking back, to have been a conspiratorial gesture, as if between us the confidentiality agreement was not only words on the page but a sacred blood sealing—ah, I don't know how to put this!—as if our future together were inexplicably entwined with the fact that whatever I told her about my work, my plans for a new sequence of paintings, or the fact that I felt fraudulent on occasion, would stay tucked away in some corner of her mind forever. Yes, right. I'll die with your words still in my mind, she said, laughing lightly, shaking the contract, which rested in her hands, waiting to be passed over to me.

Like I said, it was a holiday. Grand Central was a bustle of consumption. A few tables away, in a dark corner, a homeless man was resting with his head on his bag, snoring softly. Another man—dressed in a ragged army-issue coat—was resting casually with his hip against a trash can, looking across the room while his hand, down at his side, groped steadily for some something in the trash. At another table, a woman in a bright red coat, her face still flushed from the cold, sat forlornly with a paper cup of soup in her palm, holding it high as she spooned it into her mouth. The two cops at the table across from us sat at a slightly odd angle, facing in our direction, hands flat on the tabletop, sitting straight up in what seemed to be an officious posture, glancing my way from time to time with speculative, accusatory eyes, as if they had built a case against me—based on all of the rumours, I think I thought—and were waiting to strike when the time was right. From the hip of the one closest to me the handcuffs dangled, jiggling slightly.

The contract was a single page, copied on both sides—a standard confidentiality agreement (or non-disclosure agreement) with boilerplate lingo, *heretos* and *therefores* in a stately font—that my dealer had given me to send to her, and it looked, in her fingers, feeble and delicate. Her nails were bright green and her thin fingers had small flecks of paint on one knuckle. When I looked up she looked away from me with an abstracted, vague glance, her lips pressed softly together, puckered, and then she turned and met my gaze as if to say: Look inside my skull, fucker, and you'll see where your words are going to go and you'll see, in the soft, grey matter, in that spongy matter, the exact place where I'll keep them (your words) forever, and when I'm dead, rest assured, this grey matter will decay, along with it the things you told me and the things I witnessed as your assistant. (Later, when she was in my studio in Pennsylvania, I would tell her that I felt, at times, like a half-baked Andrew Wyeth, and that at times I felt that my appropriating his life was somewhat dubious. My appropriation of Wyeth was my shtick—I'd say—the entire thing, right down to painstakingly reconstructing his 19th century schoolhouse studio at Chadds Ford on my own plot of land on Long Island, and calling most of my models Olga, and using one of his original, albeit much older now, local models. I swear, and this might seem absurd but it's true, that even there in Grand Central, with two cops seated at the table next to us, I foresaw the fact that I'd use the word shtick and then confess that I felt, at times, completely fraudulent.)

At Grand Central that afternoon, sitting down in the food court, just after she touched the contract, just before she picked it up and handed it to me, waving it in the air so that it twisted into the shape of a boat hull, I believe I said to Christina: I have a feeling that in a few weeks, most likely at my studio in Pennsylvania, which as you know is actually in Long Island, some extremely personal confessions of mine will put me in a bad light—even for you—and if that confession were to be released into the public mind, or passed on, as I explained, it would hurt my career, not only now—I mean saleswise—but also its critical reception in the future. So I'm saying now, I mean I'm telling you this now as a way to abnegate the mirror—ah, I don't know what I'm saying, I said, and right at that moment, after I spoke and before she spoke, I felt the threshold between us that had been created not only by the contract itself, which was legally binding as soon as she passed it to me, but also by the exchange we had just had and by the milieu itself, the jaunty, holiday vibe in the air, and, Jesus, it *was* in the air, the music was going and commerce apparent in the ceremonial bustle of movement up the escalator over her head, and in and out of doorways to my right as folks poured out of trains and headed to the streets and, some of them, up Fifth Avenue to some event at Rockefeller Center. Gifts were being purchased, wrapped up, tucked into bags and conveyed to the station while we sat together having our meeting, making a secretive, totally incognito mutual agreement. There wasn't a boundary between us, but rather a threshold just above her mouth, starting at her lips and spreading to her nose and up to her eyes and then out to her ears, which months later, I imagined as I sat there, I might attempt to kiss while she stood listening to me at the window in the studio. A threshold through which my words would pass, entering the confines in which they would rest forever so long as she maintained the terms of the contract, which I gently unfolded and turned over as I examined her signature: the aggressive looping curl of her C and the soft snakes of her S and the cross of her I tapering off to a tiny A, as if her strength had given out at the end. In general it was a weak signature. It started strong but flagged in the end.

What else can I do—I believe I thought—but entrust myself to this signature and these clauses and the expression she gives of being willing to hold my words and actions and to retain them, to refuse to release them into the world? And then I said, I think, Look, you'll also have to keep to yourself—I mean as part of this agreement—everything you see, not only in my workspace but in the house and out in the field. My process, I mean. You'll have to keep quiet about that, I said, and then I sat there and imagined that we'd go out to the stone wall and follow it slowly for an entire afternoon, quietly (a brisk, but relatively bleak autumn afternoon, with a long scrim of clouds smearing the western horizon, at the bottom of the slough), trying to find the exact right subject for my next study. I'd have her put an old whaling oar on the top of the wall. I already knew this, sitting there in Grand Central. I imagined us walking together in that quiet reverie as I pondered the wall and she, in turn, pondered me as I pondered the wall, as I searched for an inspirational quirk in the set of the stones, the handiwork of some lonely man a hundred years ago, some farmer with resolve and grit, a clenched-mouthed man with a furrowed brow and whiskers on his chin and that weather-beaten, New England, wiseacre gravitas. (Like Wyeth, I saw faces in the corn! I saw a toothless man in a stalk without the kernels exposed! I saw a toothy woman in peeled back folds exposing kernels!)

Christina sat across from me with her face suddenly serene, and a slight down of peach fuzz on her upper cheeks and her earlobes. She had fantastic lobes. They were pendulous and out of proportion to her delicate ears, but not in a way that detracted—somehow, miraculously, I later thought—from the symmetry, which much later would remind me for some reason of the shape of the contract itself just before she handed it over. (If I have one talent, it's an acute memory for shapes, for the strange, intricate spaces between objects. I can still remember a particular set of stones in a wall not far from a small town called Edale, in England's Peak District, where I went in the summer to sketch some studies before I officially began to appropriate Andrew Wyeth. I remember the path and the cattle gate, with the MIND THE GATE sign, and the way the fields spread up into a sharp grade and then, over the hump of the hill, began rolling way down into what might be called a knoll. About fifty yards from the cattle gate was a wall—built with an urgency that was visible in the set of the stones near the ground—with a spot where the mason, or farmer with great skills, had struggled to make use of two rather large stones, hedging them in, tightening them with a few filler stones, forming a gape of about two inches wide, shaped like a turnip. I still remember that turnip. Not the stones themselves, but the turnip. Just as I remember—now, here alone in my cell, as I like to call it, at the institute, as they like to call it, at the window looking down on the rubber-floored yard with the chain-link fence, where other prisoners, as I like to call them, patients, as they like to call them, smoke and clench the fence, gazing through the trees at the river beyond the roar of the parkway—the exact shape of her lobes in the stale light of the food court.) I imagined in Grand Central that we'd take a direct flight together to Manchester, hire a cab to Edale, and walk that wall at a ridiculously slow pace, and that I'd stop and explain to her that I would know what I was looking for when I saw it, and that I was trying as best I could to get into the obsessive, somewhat reclusive, isolated mind of Wyeth. I'd explain (and I think I did explain) that my goal was to find a state that was even *more* obsessive and pernickety than Wyeth's. I'd like to go beyond my capacity to be Andrew Wyeth and in pushing beyond his somewhat narrow, obsessive concentration on his subjects—rolling fields and walls and his models, always lonely looking, slightly abject—I'd surpass him so that if you dialled back in order to account for the fact that I was only appropriating him, I would land squarely on actually being him. I'd explain all of this and then I'd remain silent (and I think I did remain silent) for another hour or so while I waited for the light to shift down into the bottom of the so-called slough. (It wasn't really a slough. A slough is a swamp. But this was the lowland at the dip in the valley where water often collected.) She'd sit on the ground with her legs tucked beneath her—Christina style—and her head back slightly, craning her neck while I made quick, preliminary studies, lifting my hand up after each stroke with a flourish, making sure she saw absolute concentration and commitment to the end of each stroke.

Your duty, I'd explain as we walked along the wall in Edale, is to watch me work and to record it all in your head and to hold it inside forever without revealing it to anyone, as stipulated in the contract you handed me in Grand Central, and in that manner other people—buyers, art collectors—will feel, without knowing why, the implicit secretiveness of my endeavour at some point in the future, years hence, when all that's left of my work is the work itself and a parcel (I would use that word, parcel) of biographical information, which will include—because I'm keeping a detailed journal—our meeting in Grand Central and our written agreement, sealed not only in ink but also in my lust and desire, because I'll record that, too, just as I'll record that we worked together for years in a union of mutual silence, a marriage of sorts, and that biography will include the fact that you went to your grave—as you said you would—with my secrets. Far in the future your presence in my working life will add not only an element of glamour—is there anything more glamorous than a confidentiality agreement?—but also a sense, around the vow of silence, that there was something fantastically interesting being kept at bay, forever, for eternity, I explained, as she nodded slowly, in what I mistakenly saw as a conspiratorial way, leaning forward slightly. The two cops were getting up from the table across the way, shifting their guts, moving the leather of their belts around. (Reminding me of the time the cops came to arrest my sister, arriving at the door with the same leathery shift of guts.) Down the escalator a woman came with a big red bag resting on the hand rail, and then I'm speaking again, or rather was speaking—and now I'm remembering, of course, not verbatim but as close as I can get, and I was explaining how at times, I mean times like this, I believe I qualified, I'm not sure how much real life can bear art and art real life, because the two entwine themselves only up to a delicate thin line (or point) where memory, desire, and touch start to move away from each other, repelled by the present moment, and then I reached out and took her hand, held it for a minute, and then regally kissed the tops of each of her knuckles and then the tip of each of her fingers, while she seemed—it seems to me now—to hold herself still in a way that reminded me then and, I imagined, would remind me again and again for some reason, not only of that day in Edale when we would walk along the wall, but also innumerable other moments, mainly in my studio back in Chadds Ford, when I would stand back from a painting and try to get a perspective—that ochre, pale dusky light coming through the windows!—while she sat off to the side, quietly (perhaps even bitterly) observant, holding herself at a remove (she had that kind of beauty. She struck delicately quiet poses—with her back straight and her hands at her sides, or on her knees—that seemed to speak of desolate isolation) in a pose that would remind me of Emily Dickinson; the same primness of her visage, a beautiful, resilient tightness in her pose. As I kissed her fingers—weirdly, awkwardly—she presented for the first time that pose. Then, as she listened to my apology, as I explained to her that it wouldn't happen again and that the agreement she had signed in no way excused me from any kind of abhorrent behaviour, which of course she would *not* have to keep secret. (Abhorrent behaviour towards you, I explained. Not towards the work, or towards others, or towards the landscape so to speak, I believe I said.) I was anticipating moments of rash destruction to come, because even there—amid that holiday cheer, the tight clip of heels against the smooth floors, the wonderfully anachronistic announcements of the train departures, and the police, who were now getting up from the table, still looking our way—I had a sense that the signed and sealed document on the table between us would allow for certain shared secrets that might or might not cause a tear in the fabric of the universe (call it love, call it whatever you want) on some future date, when whatever she saw and heard was eaten up by worms, or dust, in the boney emptiness of her beautifully shaped skull as it rested beneath the earth. I'll admit now with full candour that it was an absurdly grand and arrogant thought. It was the kind of thought (I thought) that you could only have in a train station during the holiday season with a beautiful young woman across from you (or a man) who had just signed away whatever secrets you might bestow upon them. It was the kind of thought that brought fire to the mind—for a few seconds—and then fell away into the category of that which is absurd but at the same time true. It was the kind of thought, I thought, that Andrew Wyeth might have had at dawn, as he departed his studio with his sketchbook in hand, while the earth gave off a soft roil of steamy vapor that hid the distant hills and seemed to bring the stone walls closer as he took it all in, feeling honestly established in that landscape, with a sense of agency (a word, I admit, he'd never use), full ownership that came from his ability to paint it in his own manner. It was Andrew Wyeth's thought and my thought at the same time, as I turned back to the business at hand—my own voice growing authoritative and firm—and went into the finer details of what I'd expect from her as my assistant in the year to come, explaining again, at the risk of redundancy, how rumours might get out, free-floating, shape-shifting, eager to form the perfect case against me as they pass from mind to mind.

Solely

Sun (only begotten)
throwing flares, not
shade, sinking behind
mountains, down couch-
backs like a pocket of
coppers, uniquely (like
a ukulele would) but
together, in an unco-
ordinated metallic rain.
Your being fructified
by a womb (not made)
gives you special essence,
exchangeable for worship.
Save some, rummage round
the couch springs; you may
find one day you are a made
man, needing unguent protection.

Ellen Dillon

Temporarily and witlessly

ignoring business, the public poet borrows
time with interest & vice versa, finds his
home in danger of repossession, no longer
worth the hoard of words he drew down against
its future value. He's been protesting, too much,
against metaphor & not enough with simile.
There are no waves, pebbles or shore—just an
ever-lengthening slime-flow seeking a sea to
slither under where there is none. The Dyno-Rod
guy said this foundational seepage was a new form
of attack. So do our hastily assembled minutes end.

Ellen Dillon

BORDER VOICES

The following collaborative commission was initiated in response to a series of tweets by James Conor Patterson, in which he decried the lack of writers from the Irish border being asked to write about the border. The commission asked five writers from the Irish border to consider their interaction with the themes and realities of borders in general, with the notion of 'voice' in mind. This collaborative sequence of 'border voices' is the result.

moving home

The autumn air is burnt. The window permits its unfreshness. A French restaurant on the corner that will do a whole camembert in baby teeth breadcrumbs. A shop that sells a string-legged doll a Nintendo 64 a ceramic tiger it's a conceptual maelstrom. Look – three Tammy green parakeets point stationwards across the sky. He knows it is time to leave and that night he writes as much on his inner thigh with a finger. [*Who shal rule the ile from the North to the South sey*] There's an illustrious cow at home. A gift for elfland queen. Milk and honey rest in its innards like water and oil and it will be used to feed a stolen child. The cow will low. In the Renaissance imagination islands sat / places of danger / reminders / uncertainties of boundaries. An illustrious cow will low.

Susannah Dickey [SD]

yew

at which point the saint lifted
a fallen aril and placed it in his alb
 carrying it for miles until he reached

the head of a desolate valley strand
 whereupon seeing only growths
of sweetbriar in the mottled sand

 he removed the thing and placed it
in a small hole invoking   *though*
only the smallest of seeds yet growing

 shall become the tallest of all things
during which time the aril split
and a yew burst slowly into life

 ruffling the sweetbriar & patrick s stole
pointing its way toward heaven & crying
 my god   this is where i m rooted

James Conor Patterson [JCP]

persephone

The myth of Persephone derives from a pre-Greek story of abduction. She was forcibly taken from her family, and Hades tricked her into eating pomegranate seeds before she was returned to her mother. Having tasted food of the Underworld, she was condemned to forever spend a third of the year below ground. At the start and end of winter, she crossed the River Styx, which marks the boundary between the world of the living and the dead.

Rivers make natural thresholds. From the hills above Derry, it seems obvious that the Foyle would be the best natural border between North and South, instead of the winding illogical line that drags through the middles of farms, skirting and crossing roads.

Crossings are known by natural and human markers: waterways and trees and concrete bollards. A marker that I will always remember is Fanny Wylie's Bridge; barely a bump in the road, a stream that dictates where the two counties meet. I have no idea who Fanny was, but it was here that I arranged to meet the first boy I ever kissed. Tracksuit bottoms tucked into socks, he had cycled with his friend from Burt, a good hour away by bike, deeper into Donegal. His friend waited on the bridge with their bikes as we walked hand in hand up the hill to a little bit of forest where there was a pheasant coop. I can still feel the soft dirt ground underfoot.

Emily S. Cooper [EC]

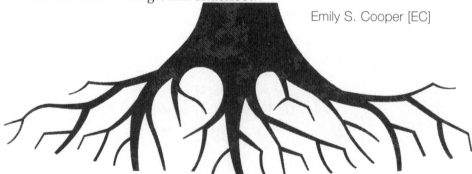

stiff green curtains

All this talk about hard and soft borders reduces the issue of the Northern Irish border to an economic issue. Queues of trucks, the interruption to business, stockpiling medicines. Farmers. Tourism. Smuggling. This MBA-media jargon is the safest way of avoiding other grosser, half-digested realities about the border. The main one being that the border was always much more than a physical infrastructure. To look back at what it was like, those tall stiff dark green curtains half-pulled across the roads, the godless proscenium in the fields, we run the risk of forgetting the border never really went away.

The dismantling of the Derry/Donegal border began illegally in 1994 with the IRA ceasefire. It happened spontaneously, the people from the area felt an itch in their hands. They plucked and tore and dug and pulled at the weakened monster. Crowds gathered to watch. The soldiers, bored, repaired the damage in the evening under floodlight. This hilarious game went on for a few weeks until the British Secretary of State, Patrick Mayhew, signed an executive order opening the roads for real. It was a fairy-tale wonder to see the helicopters carrying bits of the thing away.

The struggle against power is the struggle of memory against forgetting. In Milan Kundera's *The Book of Laughter and Forgetting*, a young grieving widow, Tamina, will find herself imprisoned on an island of children. Naked, excited, these children will demand she join in their games. At first Tamina will resist, her grief too much of a burden. But the island is a place 'back in time,' where her husband never died, and her acquiescence is not far off. The children will swarm over her nudity—'she could not tell whose hand or mouth belonged to whom.' As the time passes, takes its toll, will she grow guilty about her forgetting? One day after deliberately spoiling the game, the children will turn on her. Now the physical signs of her adulthood have become the focus of their scorn. Tamina will run and run until the children catch her and truss her up in nets. Force her back into their little games. Watching them, these naked, happy children, as they roll their hips in a mime of intercourse, lewdness superimposed on their childish bodies, Tamina will feel the destruction of the dichotomy between obscenity and innocence. Horrified, she will try to escape, jump into the water, swim for it, only to sink eventually below the spreading surface.

One peculiar effect of the border's deconstruction was amnesia. We played and sang like children without a past. It was boring and miserly and it was morbid to be caught remembering anything that had happened before the Good Friday Agreement. Before too long no-one was sure if there had ever been a border. Where was the evidence? The admissible proof? Time, like history, is a tale told by the childlike victors. We were given permission to stop remembering. Permission was imposed on us. Don't look back. Don't be a victim. Dive into the future, where the past is as kitsch as seaweed. Flow into the infantile ever-present future.

Sean O'Reilly [SOR]

economic uncertainty

Tam buys a packet of wispa bites and a packet of cheese
& onion for elfland queen and 20
of unleaded. A white doe and a white stag stand
in the forecourt. Skimmed milk / opal / lisfannon sky.
They lap from patches of poisonous rainbow. Elfland queen takes
a bite of petrol station apple. *All the diseases of hell are on this don't
you think* she says. Tam holds the pump like an off
banana squeezes reluctantly. Tam puts in 3
more than what he paid for. Tam can't tell lies. That doesn't stop
him driving away.

SD

Court the country but marry at home!

The modern tradition of the groom carrying the bride over the threshold has its roots in a Roman myth—The Rape of the Sabine Women—when women from around Rome were abducted en masse, forced into marriage, and dragged into new homes by the soldiers of the newly formed city. Like the Styx for Persephone, the threshold of the marital home became the marker of movement from one life to another, whether willing or unwilling.

I am the product of a mixed marriage of sorts. My father was born and bred in Belfast, my mother in Donegal. In the scheme of things it's a very short distance, but it might as well have been a different world. Daddy left Belfast as a teenager and never went back, finding my Mammy in the Drift Inn in Buncrana while she was home for Christmas one year. He lured her from a stool by the fire to a party with hot whiskies after boasting about his sports car (which he couldn't drive in the snow). Off they went to Dublin, then Libya, then eventually London where I spent my early years. As little Irish children in London we were sung songs as Gaeilge and taught rhymes:

> Where do you come from? *Donegal.*
> How's your purdies? *Big and small.*
> How do you eat them? *Skin and all.*
> Do they not choke you? *Not at all.*

You can understand why we were a little confused. When we arrived back home in 1997, it was to a new North. The checkpoints were being dismantled, we were sent to an integrated school and settled in a tumbling old farmhouse just on the Derry side of the border.

EC

dead letter office

There is no patron saint of cartographers. You will not find the position on any of the floors or along any of the corridors. It is a blind-spot, even in the department that allocates patron saints to new inventions and developments: virtual reality, nanotechnology, artificial memories. Whether it is simply overlooked or deliberately forbidden has never been established, but all prayers relating to mapmaking end up filed, undelivered, in the Dead Letter Office. There they gather dust for all eternity. Stacks of papers. Audio files. They are rarely visited but it is possible, with the right permits. You could spend several lifetimes sifting through the records. George Bass, crazed and enslaved, carving words on the walls in the depths of a Chilean silver mine after being pronounced 'lost at sea' in the Pacific. Mansa Qu dying in whispers on the Mosquito Coast having set off, from Mali, to find the end of the ocean, 'never to return nor to give a sign of life.' Sometimes the messages were garbled. It was, for example, difficult to discern whether the prayers that came from a man burning to death at Toul Sleng were from John Dawson Dewhirst or his friend Kerry Hamill, both having drifted off course and into the waters of the Red Khmer.

Darran Anderson [DA]

paranoid stories

The border was always much more than its pornographic visibility. The border existed in multiple shifting dimensions. You had the sawn-off dragon's teeth [https://en.wikipedia.org/wiki/Dragon%27s_teeth_ (fortification)] blocking the back roads and the green steel curtains on the big roads beyond which lay the republic of freedom-hoarders. The border was Colditz surveillance towers in the city centre, cutting-edge zoom, infra-red, microphones which could hear the endless stirring of cups of tea (half the city comatose on the Diazepam dished out by doctors) in the homes of the Bogside and all the way up the hill to the Creggan. The border was paranoid stories of poisoned water, robot dogs, people back from the dead. The border was mobile, multiple, and moved around in armed patrol squads and screaming six-wheeled murder machines. The border was a military grid system draped like a shroud over the chimneys. The border choked and curdled and seared and put hands in your pockets and berets in your dreams. The border was a smashed front door, a weaponised soldier in your bedroom, your pillow in the street. The border was the supernatural gap between what you might have witnessed on the street and what you might see on the TV news a few hours later. The edit. The angle. The difference, the loss. The occupation by the obscene not even the mighty cathedral bells could dispel.

SOR

internment

clegs & fuckin

blue arsed flays

stun themselves fatly

against the tobacco

stained porthole

above my door

out on derrybeg drive

a couple of kids

are draggin a roll

of chain link fence

off a concrete post

and up by main avenue

heaney s snug as a gun

is bein tapped out

in stones & bottles

against a paint covered

saracen soon

they ll be here

to smash

my ma s old bureau

to crack the sacred heart

with their boot heels

to stick their rifle butts

through the sittin room

cabinet where i ve kept

my a o h sash pinned

to its backboard

like a moth

balled weddin dress

for twenty five years

down there for dancin

ye brit cunts

my heart exploded

two days ago

durin grandstand

and all you ll find now

is a stack of old papers

a teacup brimmin

with mould

a tartan quilted

shoppin trolley

and my grey face

grinnin up from the shag

to the bin lidded

chorus at st brigid s

JCP

archangels at work

This is not to say that maps were not worked on. Given that everything that ever happened was recorded, so too were changes in cartography. Rows of archangels with gawping mouths and eyes filled with golden cataracts summoned up topographies before them, like holograms but tangible, feeling their way along the gradients like braille. These were formed and discarded upon the dissolution of countless states and nations and lay in corners like sculptures lost in transit—the Mountainous Republic of the Northern Caucasus for one, the Ryukyu Kingdom another. At times, the border lines felt like fractures on bone. At other times, ever-changing at times of battle for instance, they took real skill to discern. Borders like oil dropped into water.

For all the archiving, the archangels paid no attention to the lives that unfolded on the borders. They cared nothing for the limbo of those who found themselves stateless. They charted the change of the German internal border from the death zone of watchtowers and barbed wire to a greenbelt that snaked through the country, but they recorded nothing of those killed on the wire. A little boy washed up face-down on a beach was none of their concern. Nor are the border coyotes, between Mexico and the United States, hanging victims' underwear from 'rape trees'. They cared nothing for those who dreamt up the borders to begin with or how such fictions became real, or who profits and who bears the cost.

DA

transitions

On the day I was born, my parents travelled from the Central Bar in Letterkenny, through the checkpoint, for me to be born in Altnegelvin in Derry. The story of my birth was one of my father's favourites—'Let me tell you about *The Day You Came Into This World'*. His romantic tale involved swans on the Swilly and nurses joking about me becoming a football player because my kicks were so strong. He left out the parts about him being fed sandwiches so he'd be sober enough to drive her through the checkpoint, and how the cord wrapped around my neck and how they cut Mammy wide open down her belly and left a scar so big that I have no memory of ever seeing her midriff. I did not make an easy transition into this world.

Daddy made an easier transition out, there was very little blood and he controlled every aspect of his care until we were able to drive him back across the same border crossing (without a checkpoint) to be buried in Donegal. Not his home, but where he chose to be.

EC

the origins of home

The cartographer is named George. He's a Catholic but his mother is from London. He says his mates are called Giovanni and Lazarus and Fausto but no relation to that Lazarus or that Faustus. There's a photo of the four of them stuck to the fridge. *Stag do at Mona* George says. *Took ages to find it.* *Puerto Rico* Tam asks. *Wales* George says. George says Ireland is the most alarming island of all. *Why is it at the top of the map* Tam wants to know.

Occidens George says.

L'Occitane elfland queen says.

No George says.

Do you mean 'by accident' Tam says.

No George says.

SD

truth

The border has endured beyond the end of Operation Banner, the British Army name for their campaign in Northern Ireland, 1969 – 1998. It can still be seen in the cover-ups and lies about what happened during those decades, the British State's refusal to deal honestly with the question of legacy. The border is now about justice, about who gets to tell their story, about the right to a memory. The forgotten now haunt the edges of a dubious jurisdiction. To get some sense of what the border looks like now, put down your copy of *The Stinging Fly* and go to the homepage of the Pat Finucane Centre in Derry [http://www. patfinucanecentre.org]. Named after the Belfast solicitor executed by the British State in cahoots with the UDA, this is a support and information centre for any family bereaved by the Troubles, north or south. Spend a few minutes exploring the headings: Human Rights – Truth Recovery – Declassified Documents. Read about the lies around the murder of 11-year-old Stephen McConomy and 15-year-old Paul Whitters by soldiers using plastic bullets, even after their own scientists said the weapons weren't safe. Read about the slaughter of 11 people in Ballymurphy by the same Parachute Regiment who carried out Bloody Sunday a few months later. Consider the meaning of the RoLMA project:

Objectives

The Recovery of Living Memory Archive (RoLMA) is committed to the following objectives:

1. To ensure that victims' families and survivors receive the maximum permissible disclosure of information regarding the death/s of their relative/s from those statutory agencies tasked with investigating historic conflict related fatalities on both sides of the border and where appropriate information about incidents where survivors were injured.

2. To ensure that the human impact of the bereavement and the biographical background of the victim is recorded.

3. To narrow the list of questions passed from generation to generation following a violent death and thereby lessen the impact of trans-generational trauma.

4. To collaborate with families in the production of an all-encompassing document that will record for posterity the factual background to the incident, the subsequent impact on survivors but also the positive biographical story of someone's life.

5. To make the final reports publicly accessible.

6. To provide a template on how to bridge the gap between storytelling and truth recovery. It is hoped that this will provide valuable learning on how to deal with the legacy of the conflict in a more holistic way.

7. To lessen the impact of the marginalization experienced by victims/ survivors in the Republic who have been excluded to date from the development of policy and practice in respect of victims' issues.

8. Provide skills sharing workshops for other support organisations in order to build capacity throughout the sector in advocacy and advice skills. In particular PFC will provide skills sharing with those groups more likely to gain the confidence of those in Protestant/ unionist/ loyalist community who wish to engage with statutory bodies.

9. Develop informal support networks among families bereaved by the conflict and, where appropriate signpost people to appropriate support services.

10. Creating a model for addressing the impact of conflict for use by the wider community, locally and internationally.

If you really want to know about what the border feels like then dig in deeper into some of the publications by the centre [http://www.patfinucanecentre.org/publications/impact-parachute-regiment-belfast-1970-73] or the pamphlet available online [http://spinwatch.org/images/Countergangs1971-76.pdf] about the methods employed by the British Army, the use of killing gangs for example.

Military Reaction Forces (MRF's) were groups of military assassins, plainclothes, unmarked cars, driving around the north executing anybody who took their fancy in order to stir up trouble, especially if there was any rumour of peace-talks going on. The murders committed by these gangs were not simply due to badly disciplined soldiers on a rampage but were institutional and deliberate and approved by those at the highest levels of the British State.

The main architect behind this counter-insurgency theory was a man called Brigadier Frank Kitson. Educated at Stowe, a public school with a stated ambition to produce a new cadre of defenders of the Empire, Kitson served in colonial wars in the 1950s and 1960s including the EOKA-led Greek nationalist uprising against British rule in Cyprus. He wrote a book called *Low Intensity Operations* about his experience of war in the far-off colonies, which he then put into practice on the streets of Northern Ireland. This was followed by *Bunch of Fives* and *Gangs and Counter-Gangs* (currently available from Faber & Faber). The content of these books can be narrowed down to four main principles: Control of the population/Covert Operations/ Special Units/ Psyops. Behind these words you will discover the nightmare logic of some of the most sickening and indiscriminate murders during Operation Banner (Operation Helvetica from 1998 to the present). The British State continues to mythologise the role of the army in Northern Ireland, while crushing the hopes of victims and their families for a story they can tell themselves, a story containing the names of those responsible, those who pulled the trigger and those who ordered it. Kitson was the man in charge of Para 1, the bunch of soldiers who destroyed innocent people in Ballymurphy and Derry, for which he was awarded a CBE and would eventually in 1982 become Commander-in-Chief, UK Land Forces.

In 2015, a woman by the name of Mary Keenan, accompanied by her son Eugene, climbed the steps of the Ministry of Defence in London to serve a writ on the MOD and Kitson for complicity in the murder of her husband, Paddy Keenan. Paddy Keenan was killed when a grenade was thrown onto a bus by Protestant paramilitaries. The ex-soldier charged with the murder, Albert 'Ginger' Baker, claimed to have links with British Intelligence and was a member of the Romper Room Gang, known to have carried out at least 22 murders. It is the first attempt to hold a high-ranking officer responsible for anything in the history of the Troubles. This is where the real border starts to get dismantled.

SOR

[http://www.patfinucanecentre.org][http://www.patfinucanecentre.org/publications/impact-parachute-regiment-belfast-1970-73] [http://spinwatch.org/images/Countergangs1971-76.pdf]

labour club regulars

there we were   sat hunkered around the scorched end of a woodbine gasper waiting for d'arcy & discussing the horses we said things like *we re all beaten dockets here son* and *stand us one paddy and i'll get ye when i'm solvent* because as paddy well knew the luck of us men was perpetually on its way   having its progress hampered by critical looks from the omniscient wife   or being decanted down storm drains by paras who blocked off roads & butchered dogs by men who damaged heirlooms & battered children anyone could see these were hard times and when d arcy finally appeared he was wearing a moth eaten crombie and his face was hidden behind a reconditioned tea cosy someone told us later that he'd had a six shot revolver stuffed into his pocket others of us remembered that it was a finger pressed against the inside lining of his coat nevertheless once he waded out across the clubhouse floor he was like a buckshot goose negotiating water and it soon became clear that he intended to have us robbed the coffers of our takings in vital need of *redistribution* the excitement in his hands made manifest by their shaking and so he pipes up to no one in particular *p put yer fuckin hands up and open that there till* to which paddy responds cool as you like that if a single fucking penny went missing it'd be added to his tab and doubled three times over to which d'arcy relented and ordered a rum & black his drink blighted face still caught inside its cosy his sloped malnourished shoulders still wrapped inside their crombie

JCP

66

patron saint of border crossings

There is no patron saint of cartographers but there is one for border crossings; the Mexican priest Romo González, shot in the back, and transformed, impromptu, into Saint Toribio. The story goes, beyond the shrines and kitsch, Toribio waits out in the edge-lands to guide the lost and weary to safety. Some say he drives a pickup truck. Some say he carries water. Some say he knows the land as well as any map. A desperate wishful story is all it is. A mirage in human form.

DA

back seat of the car

I am in the back seat of the car, my mother at the wheel. It is not lost on me that she cannot drive. She should not be doing this. We are in a queue at the border, not far to go to the curtain, the berets. I can see her eyes in the mirror as she puts on her lipstick, the first time I've ever seen this. You keep your mouth shut, she tells me. Keep your eyes shut while you're at it. Maybe we are running away together. We move closer to the brink. She rolls down the window, leans her bare elbow out. Her freckles. Her funny bone. Now I see a hole in the floor, right between my legs. And a hole in the tarmac also. It's some kind of shaft which leads down to a tunnel under the road. The tunnel is full of squirrels, hundreds of them, going in both directions. Our car has now drawn level with a black soldier in a tiny tartan beret. Behind him a large pile of antlers. The beret leans in the window and licks his lips and says to my mother, tell me you love me darling, and my mother flashes me a warning look in the mirror and I can't bear it, I can't stand it, what she might have to say… and I wake myself up.

SOR

on Ellis Island

On Ellis Island, immigrants would shuffle off the ships and climb the stairs to be met by a doctor and a translator. They would be quickly examined for clues. If any signs or suspicions arose, their coats would be marked with cryptic letters in chalk:

> Ct: eye disease
> H: heart problems
> Pg: pregnancy

An X on the right shoulder suggested mental illness or deficiency. Further down the arm suggested a disease. A circle around the X confirmed it. In a multitude of languages, those who wore the mark of chalk began to quietly pray to the gods they'd brought with them.

DA

he writes elfland queen a poem

At the bottom of a garden a small river flits like a blood vessel. A woman comes to bear witness. The old couple who own the garden eat sandwiches throw

crusts into the river. The woman asks that they stop feeding it. [It will soon become uncontrollably large.] The purple bubbles on the river's surface grow

darker with each new thought. The old woman dips her hands in it watches it smooth the deep rivulets in her skin. The younger woman never ventures

in never dips her feet in its linens. [If I wanted physical intimacy the river would still be a man.] The old couple watch the river camouflage

itself in the navy air. The young woman is a giant has a deep bleeding wound in her head. The moon looks like a cataract. It fires mountain-sized

shadows but never hits its target. How long have we been doing this the old woman asks the old man. The fridge hums. I've always liked

crusts the old man says. I wish someone would pity us, the old woman says.

SD

other borders

There are other borders than those between countries. There are those between life and death, between one person and another. That's just the way of things, as immutable as the border between one place and another. That's what they tell themselves. And they are we.

DA

the wounded knee incident

with carragher pinwheeling around the wounded knee
on church st   *because the father says so   e yayo*
    i d have thought this ghost dance might curb the madness
now rippling through him like a deafening salvo

        forgive me   a*té*   for i ve not been entirely honest
        here   though knees are shucked like mountain oysters
    piss stained tweeds stand in for feathers & calico

        each night   our enemies are backwashed into a short
    and the blood of your   my   ancestors is gurgled in retort

JCP

remember your voice

Daša Drndić was obsessed by names. People are forgotten only if and because their names are forgotten. In book after book, she used a radical bricolage to weaken the border between fact and fiction, arguing that our child-like inattention to history is responsible for what we continue to do to each other, again and again, within and across national boundaries. In *Trieste*, she listed the names of Italian Jews over forty pages, in *Belladonna* a list of 2,061 Jewish children deported from the Netherlands to camps between 1938 and 1945 and in *E.E.G.* the names and biographies of the chess-playing victims of Nazism. 'Memory and space,' she writes, 'are in a permanent clinch; when space collapses, it drags memory into its underground, into its non-existence, and without memory, the present becomes sick, mutilated, a torso with amputated organs.'

Backstop or not, hard or soft, talk of a return of the border, is a nightmare Dali-esque threat to the psyche. An amputated limb sewn back on to the angelic body-politic. Melting clocks. Hideous eggs. Tigers on stilts. Bone-like trees. Lakes of glassy semen. Eyes in hands. The paranoid-critical method Dali called his process. Let your fears show you the truth. The border is a big snake digesting a statue. The border is a judge's wig which squeezes through your letterbox at night and flops up the stairs. The border is the blades of the sun and the telescopic moon. The border is a castle without a single window. Tourette streetlights. Your father back from another arrest but like honey he sticks to the furniture, the tinted glass walls. The border is a defaced dictionary stuffed down the back of a fire-damaged sofa in a field of spears topped with the skulls of each and every one of your memories. The traumatic déjà vu of a new border, the monstrous return, the hideous re-enactment, threatens the fragile grip on reality of those of us who have done our best to forget.

Forget the trucks, forget about business just for one bloody second. Remember your voice.

Remember to keep saying what happened.

SOR

fourteen years later

The people will always find new ways of splitting
water. Lobster catchers and canoes and shopping
trolleys. [A river is no kind of thing to have
in common.] The bank is black and partisan and held in
place with undesirable net and metal. Where were you when he
went in? Do you remember how we'd forgotten
to remember where he'd been? One woman
saw two golden retrievers that could have been a stag or a doe
or both. [This river flows hard. It is a monster's mouth
drawn in our own likeness. It severs like a lobotomy
severs.] Four antlers and three heads go under the meringue'd
foam of water's surface. It's too soon for the helicopters.

SD

Las Meninas

A world peopled with images,
what else would a painter paint?

*

Being's joinery,
it appears,

serves not
to compartment—

the screens, doors,
mirrors, frames,

space by space,
extending.

*

How else might a dwarf wait
near a princess, but by partitions?

Or a retainer
cross a foot
to a dog's back?

Or decorated Velázquez
deliberate on
royal shadows,

fixed in their place,
looking
as we look?

Fergal Gaynor

Nothing Can Dislodge The House

Martina Evans

> *Nothing can dislodge*
> *the house with my first tooth*
> *noosed in a knot to the doorknob.*
> —Robert Lowell

> *The human mind is a mass of associations—associations more poetic than*
> *actual... Location is the crossroads of circumstance, the proving ground of*
> *'What happened? Who's here? Who's coming?'—and that is the heart's ground.*
> —Eudora Welty

I'm in Burnfort Bar, County Cork. It's 1977. Taking The Eagles, *Greatest Hits, 1971-1975* cassette out of its blue case. I insert it into the white plastic tape recorder and press the chunky cube of the play button. 'Hotel California' fills the air with its dark glamour, summoning up a shadowy highway in the desert—a faster-moving moody world. The wind flies through someone's hair and there is a warm smell of 'coolitas'. A mission bell sounds, 'This could be heaven or this could be hell'. My own world stands still to allow it in.

When I say Burnfort Bar, I mean the whole building, not just the bar but the grocery shop and the rooms where we live. I am in the room we call the dining room but it's really a living room, although we hardly have time to sit there. The sitting room is upstairs and even less used. Its door is marked with an ivory plate which reads 114. Burnfort Bar was originally owned by a scrap merchant called Dan Kirk—reminders of his salvage are everywhere, like the railway tracks which support the kitchen ceiling. Daddy stores nails and rusty screws and bits of string in the high ledge formed by the tracks near the ceiling. Daddy is also a fervent believer in salvage and doesn't like to part with anything, especially his old clothes, to which he is pathologically attached.

A massive marble fireplace with black and white tiles illustrated with Grecian figures commands the dining room, and an even larger fireplace—a complicated mahogany contraption with shelves and drawers—takes up one wall of the sitting room. When I was seven, I stood on a chair to get my colour pencils from one of those drawers and the fireplace moved at my touch. Terrified, I withdrew my hand immediately, but with a great sigh like a judgement, the entire edifice shifted further away from the damp wall. My older sister helped me to hold it up as we screamed for help. I was sick with the fear of getting into trouble and full of shame when someone found the stale buttered cream crackers which I'd stored in the drawer with my colour pencils. I can't remember what happened after that—the rest of the incident has disappeared along with the fireplace. Memories are full of holes, it's hard to find the thread that connects.

The upstairs floor of the house is lined with dark pine panelling. There are five doors with ivory doorknobs and each door has an ivory plate with a number, starting with Room 110, ending with 114. They say that they came from a hotel, although later someone else says that they are from a luxury ocean liner that crashed off the coast of East Cork. A hotel floating on the sea.

Many-roomed houses or hotels, further extensions of Burnfort Bar, have always dominated my dreams. They segue with certain books and films until I can't separate between them: Thornton Manor from *Jane Eyre*, Wuthering Heights, the Overlook Hotel from *The Shining*, The Majestic from *Troubles*, Bly from *The Turn of the Screw*, the castle in *The Pit and the Pendulum* and especially *Twin Peaks'* Great Northern Hotel. I often dream of shops too, versions of our grocery shop have begun to merge with the *Twin Peaks'* convenience store. The convenience store has gasoline pumps in front, like Burnfort Bar with its yellow and green BP pump in our front yard. There is a tall BP sign too, swinging on a chain, creaking in the wind. In my dreams, Burnfort Bar is the entry to other worlds, in the same way that *Twin Peaks'* convenience store is the portal to an alternative world. Towards the end of Season Three, Gordon

Cole says, 'We are like the dreamer who dreams and then lives inside the dream, but who is the dreamer?' My dreams have become so entangled with The Great Northern Hotel and the convenience store that sometimes I wonder if David Lynch is dreaming me or if I'm dreaming him.

Like the maze, the house is often seen as a representation of the psyche, with its locked doors, dead ends. It usually contains some version of the minotaur, like *The Shining*'s Jack Torrance with its unforgettable image of Jack Nicholson's lowered bull-like head. When we grow up we forget about the minotaurs but children know all about them. Smaller than everyone else, at the mercy of grown-ups—they know that fears kept in locked rooms by day spring out twice as deranged by night.

Back in 1977, I am singing along to 'Hotel California', loving but not understanding its ambiguous lyrics: 'You can check out any time you like but you can never leave.' Forty years later, the lines are eerily appropriate seeing as I physically checked out of Burnfort Bar many years ago.

The old dining room is a thoroughfare, a crossroads which links our private space with the public space of the bar and the shop. Of its three doors, one leads to the shop, one to the kitchen and the other to the hall and stairs. The table is always heaped with books and papers, a bowl of plastic fruit, messages that have been put away for customers. Mrs Callaghan from Knuttery's three sliced pans sit on the table every Saturday night, waiting for her arrival after Second Mass on Sunday. I rush to give them to her because I love Mrs Callaghan. 'Aren't you great!' she says with such kindness that I believe it. I desperately want to be told that I am great. Growing up 'in the public eye', as Mammy calls it, can be hard.

The tablecloth is soft and dark and velvety. It softens the clatter of the silver cash box where all the money is put at the end of the night. A couple of times a week, Mammy takes the lodgement to the Bank of Ireland in Mallow. She can turn the car around on her own these days but when I was younger, my sister and I dreaded the moment we had to walk up to strangers on Main Street, saying, 'Excuse me, my mother's just learnt to drive. Could you turn the car and face it for home, please?' My sister blames the school bus-driver Jimmy Nyhan, who urges Mammy with the passionate intensity he put into everything he did: 'Never be afraid, Mrs Cotter, to ask a man for help!'

There's no one around now. It's hard to be unobserved here but I feel confident enough to sing along for a moment. I have no idea what coolitas are, but I love the sound of them the way I love the sound of Kool Aid when I come across it in American books. I think Kool Aid is some kind of cooling medicine until I realise that the characters are just quenching their thirst—something that happens a lot in Burnfort Bar.

All kinds of bottles line the shelves in the bar and the shop and the Bottle Shed where Daddy and I often raise big heavy flagons to our lips—Daddy drinking Bulmer's Woodpecker cider and me drinking Cidona. These forbidden apples are irresistible. There is also Tanora, Fanta Orange, Fanta Lemon and Clockhouse Red Lemonade, Taylor Keith, Miwadi and more. The ads for these drinks convince me that somewhere else people are living the life. Especially the Coke ads, which make me yearn heavily. But Kool Aid is a mystery. It can take years to find out what something means.

The Spanish word 'coolitas' is generally believed to refer to the pine-smelling cannabis buds of California. Back in 1977, I know nothing about drugs. Maybe coolitas refers to Coca Cola, which I love. Mammy abhors 'soft drinks' above everything else. 'The citric acid!' She doesn't allow us to eat sweets either but we can have as much fruit as we want. There isn't much of a selection though—just oranges, bananas and those golden delicious apples which should be crisp but rarely are.

Despite the distinct lack of coolitas in my world, I'm often told that I'm 'like someone drugged' and berated for going around in a dream, my head in a book. I am the youngest of ten children and everyone is older, siblings and customers. By 1977 I've been drinking black coffee for seven years—ever since I gave up milk and sugar for Lent. A family meeting—the only one I ever remember—is held on the subject of my coffee drinking. What galls one brother is the way I don't even use a spoon, just shake the jar of Maxwell House instant granules into my mug with a flick of my wrist. This brother is known to come home drunk but this isn't for me to say. That would be 'trying to be smart'. That would be 'not funny'. It's better that I keep quiet, transport myself to alternate worlds, 'check out' with books or music.

When ultra-intense Agent Cooper turns up in the town of Twin Peaks in 1990, shamelessly obsessed with coffee, cherry pie and dreams, champion of all those isolated slightly-crazed women, sensitive yet with no fear whatsoever of being smart, how could I not love him? And who doesn't love a murder mystery?

We are all detectives in a way, following some thread through a maze. When I was younger, I'd hoped to find a secret passage behind the upstairs panelling and spent many hours tapping and measuring but of course there was nothing behind the salvaged façade. There is a real secret passage in The Great Northern Hotel, where Audrey Horne peers through a hole at her 'wicked' father. My splintered memories seem a little like that now—fragments glimpsed through a hole in the wall.

In the final season of *Twin Peaks*, Audrey is still tragically trapped in her past and her eyes in the mirror scene remind me of Barbara Steele's helpless eyes peering from the Iron Maiden in Roger Corman's *The Pit and the Pendulum* which I saw in the Savoy Cinema, Cork in 1968. Those eyes stared out of the pine-panelling in my bedroom for years—it might have been a trick of the pale light cast from the electric green and white Major cigarette sign outside my window but most probably it was from my own imagination. Horror experts like Henry James and Hitchcock have always known how to exploit their readers/viewers by leaving plenty of holes for the readers to fill with their own particular hells.

One-armed Mike describes The Great Northern Hotel as 'A large house, made of wood, surrounded by trees. The house is filled with many rooms, each alike, but occupied by different souls, night after night.' This reminds me of the large stand of fir trees at the end of the field behind Burnfort Bar. When I was a child I thought it was the forest.

Burnfort Bar's heavily wooded upstairs corridor feels separate from the rest of the house—like it could float off, like an ocean liner, from what's happening below—men drinking night after night, talking and singing. I longed for them to sing because when they all joined in, the bedroom filled with their voices and I was no longer afraid. The sing-songs are happening less and less in 1977. What Mammy calls 'Singing Lounges' have begun to spring up around the countryside—big barn-like places rather like The Roadhouse in *Twin Peaks*. The most talked about is The Ranch in Mallow six miles away. You just can't get away from Hollywood or cowboy films or country music, which is very popular now.

Even Burnfort Bar has saloon doors by 1977. Installed by a crooning unreliable builder, they make an awful clatter when anyone enters, so no one can slip in quietly to the toilets as I imagine they would like to do. I swagger in and out of them myself when there is no one around, demonically twirling my imaginary pistols like Lee Marvin.

The singing lounges have bands and attract large crowds. Mammy thinks they are dens of iniquity. They attract 'low types' and 'cheap Jacks', preying on the innocent fools who wander in 'trying to be with it.' I have never been inside one so I will never know now what they were really like. I have never been to a dancehall either. 'Desperate-looking,' Mammy groans when we drive past a large purpose-built concrete building with a flat roof, half way up a mountain.

The singing lounges seem to have gagged the occasional singers of Burnfort. Or maybe the singers had been attracted away like moths. Some evenings in the bar, it is so quiet our faithful customer Tom Twomey can be heard swallowing his Guinness. 'People don't sing any more,' Mammy says sadly. She's always looking backwards, in fact most of my family are looking in that direction. Everyone has a different story and so much happened before I was even born. We are the poor relations, the large family blown off course who sold 'a beautiful big farm' for no reason that anyone can agree on, and lost 'everything' in Australia. Someone must be at fault and the debate rages on even if no one can really be sure what happened and most of us weren't even born when the decision was taken.

My parents started their married life in Patrickswell, County Limerick, on a big farm which was believed to be haunted and unlucky. In 1950 they sold the farm and emigrated to Australia with five children. By the time they returned in 1960, they had nine children. I was born in 1961, one year after they arrived in Burnfort Bar with no experience of running any kind of business and no knowledge of pubs. Mammy was forty-two and Daddy was fifty-nine when they were thrust into this new world 'in the public eye.'

My parents are blow-ins—another source of isolation—both eccentric in their own way. Daddy feeds cornflakes to our pet cow Rose as local men nearly pass out laughing. He claims that Fifi the dog speaks to him occasionally, when we're not around. Mammy can't stop 'opening up' as she calls it. She wants to be reserved, urging herself and everyone else, 'For God's sake, don't be telling your life story, letting everyone know your business!' But she can't help it. Yet it works both ways because people open up to her too, or so she says with great satisfaction, distracted for a while from her own worries.

Mammy is always talking, telling stories. She has a fine sense of humour but can't take a joke. She can be perceptive and edgy but most of the time she's racked with worry and anxiety. 'When? When will it end?' she asks, or 'What does it all mean?' and we double up with laughter. But really, she must be exhausted. She is sentimental sometimes but not very often—that corner is monopolised by the heavy drinkers at the counter. And she is always dramatic in the true sense, meaning that every story she tells can be acted out. Like Dickens, who stood in front of the mirror pulling faces to make sure he got his descriptions right, she strikes poses in the dark sideboard mirror in the dining room. Dickens also liked to mix all the styles in his writing—he called it Streaky Bacon. *Twin Peaks*, with its mixture of horror, humour, melodrama, poetry and metaphysics, is Streaky Bacon too.

The County Limerick humour seems blacker, harder than the Cork humour, but maybe it is just my family. When I first began to publish poems in 1989, I wanted to use my mother's maiden name, O'Shaughnessy, but someone said it would not work. 'Too stage-Irish!' he said. To this day I'm convinced that Martina O'Shaughnessy would have had a completely different literary career, a different life. She stays there in the eighties, stillborn, forever on the fork of a road long passed. Doppelgangers and doubles, alternate worlds, the stuff of *Twin Peaks*.

Burnfort Bar is located at Burnfort Cross and crossroads represent fate. American convenience store stores are traditionally placed on crossroads too, bringing to mind those old photos of African-Americans singing the blues, playing banjo and guitar, dancing on the boards—where Robert Johnson made a deal with the devil. Places of magic and danger, sacred to Hermes, crossroads represent liminality, a place where two worlds meet.

My family is haunted by the story of their exile. Mammy speaks dolefully of the shame and sorrow of being an emigrant while Daddy smiles to himself and imitates the call of the Kookaburra—the laughing jackass. 'I never thought I'd get out of it,' Mammy says. Back then, emigrating to Australia was like going to another world, almost like the life sentence it once was when people were transported to Van Diemen's Land.

Sister Martina, a cousin of Daddy's, emigrated to Australia in 1912 when she was fourteen years old. Her father didn't want her to go but she couldn't be stopped. Her older sister—only sixteen—agreed to join the order too so that she could go along to take care of her. One of my brothers, also an exile, told me the story of Sister Martina's dream. Every night she dreamt that she was walking up the path to her old family home in County Limerick, but as soon as she put her finger on the latch of the door, she woke up. My brother struggled to finish the story but when he got to the part when she put her finger on the latch, he was choked with tears. I've never seen him cry before or since. Now I can't tell the story, can't get past the part where she puts her finger on the latch without getting a lump in my throat. Who is the dreamer? Are our minds like hotels where guests can come and go? Is this what one-armed Mike meant when he spoke of the house made of wood being 'occupied by different souls, night after night'?

The forest is another maze—like the house or hotel, another expression of the human psyche with its locked doors and dark corners. Burnfort Cross is a T-junction with roads leading North, South and East. If it were a true cross, there would have been a road through my childhood 'forest', that stand of fir trees behind the house where I played as a child when I was young enough not to be called back to work. Sometimes I really scared myself down there—I felt an unseen presence watching me, and it wasn't the ubiquitous god from my green catechism. I imagined the lurid devil from my prayer book, illustrated in black and red with his angry arrow tail.

When Sheriff Truman talks about the woods in *Twin Peaks*, he says, 'There's a sort of evil out there. Something very, very strange in these old woods. Call it what you want. A darkness, a presence. It takes many forms but… it's been out there for as long as anyone can remember.' Sheriff Truman is a stock character, a parody of the traditional white-hat hero, yet his clichéd description of the woods becomes truly terrifying if you take these woods as a metaphor for the human mind.

These days my dreams of Burnfort merge with *Twin Peaks'* formidable convenience store and I think again of Dan Kirk and all the curiosities he added to Burnfort Bar. Our minds are masters of salvage, constantly selecting and rearranging the furniture of our dreams at night. For me, David Lynch is the supreme scrap merchant. Taking the archetypes of forests, hunting, Bluebeard, rings, riddles, numbers, the maze and the minotaur and mixing them with The Book of Revelation, Old Hollywood and many popular references, he makes something fresh and new, yet uncannily familiar, as if he really is the dreamer of our dreams.

I still associate horror films with upstairs in Burnfort Bar because of the terror I experienced at night haunted by *The Pit and the Pendulum* and the first sixty pages of *The Exorcist*. Upstairs in the *Twin Peaks'* convenience store, supernatural spirits gather around a green formica table that bears plates of the creamed corn or 'Garmonbozia', which is the pain and suffering these spirits need to survive. Is this one of reasons we watch horror? Do we need to digest pain and suffering too? Can this be linked to memory? The past can be seductive, terrifying too.

Crossroads represent fate, which Rilke described as a condensation of childhood. Perhaps that is the terror—the idea that in our beginning is our end and free will really is an illusion. Who can forget Laura Palmer's scream of terror when she finally recognised her childhood home after Agent Cooper 'rescued' her from an alternative reality in Odessa, Texas? Or maybe we fear that there is no end, nothing but alternative worlds spinning out into eternity. It is ironic then that our only escape might be the transportation to other worlds in art, literature, music and film. Some of us try to make art ourselves but it's when we're asleep that our minds become really confident hunters—sorting through scrapyards, creating new and startling combinations from all the old things.

Ancestral

Louise Hegarty

The monster in the basement goes thump thump thump to remind me it's still there. As if I need reminding. As if I could possibly think of anything else. At night-time, instead of sleeping, I float through billowing rooms, tiptoe on carpeted floors and go out to the gardens to scream. Eventually I collapse into sleep until the thump thump thump comes once more and I am forced to rise and move on to another part of the house. Oh, the house. The lawns swoop and slide. The gravel whispers. The high arches loom. The gate and the pillars. The flowerbeds kept neatly by the head gardener. The panelled doors and high ceilings. The bustle in the servants' quarters. The library. The drawing room. The fireplaces. The long drive up to the house and the mature trees. And it has been twenty-one days since my father died and the peerage and the house and drive and the gravel and the lawn have passed to me thump thump thump.

This morning the valet dressed me in my father's fine tweed suit and shoes and pocket watch. He hesitated first and wondered aloud whether I would feel uncomfortable wearing the clothes of a dead man. I reprimanded him for his impertinence but what I didn't say is that I was used to it. There are photographs of me as a baby on my mother's lap, in clothes already embroidered with my older brother's initials. They didn't think anything of dressing me in the clothes he had died in thump thump thump.

The house needs a woman. That is clear. The maids do their best but really I need a wife. I need someone who knows how to run a house and who can deal with large estates and monsters. Things are changing and shifting. Thump. The house has come into my possession at a very difficult time. Thump. I just don't want to be the last. Thump. I send out some letters with instructions to find me a wife and my friends and colleagues return with letters of their own and photographs of beautiful young women through which I sift. I arrive at a shortlist of three and so I go to London on a short sojourn to meet them and their families and to judge their interest. All three ladies are lovely and appropriate but there is one in particular who catches my eye. She is pretty as a button and smiley and light and everything I am not. She even lived in Dublin briefly as a child, when her father's work brought the family there. And she tells me that their house in Yorkshire has a monster in the lake so that sort of thing doesn't bother her. Over a nightcap with her father we arrange everything. I return to Ireland and she follows soon after as my bride. Our wedding is small but expensive (as is appropriate) and my wife is beautiful in milky foamy white. I give her my mother's ring and it fits perfectly.

From the outset I know I have made the right choice: the house is reborn with her just being here. The dust clears, the rooms are brighter and the staff are energetic. Her father is a very modern sort who believes that his daughters should be well educated and able to hold their own in dinner-table conversations, so I am never bored. She also rides horses, plays a little piano and speaks good French. She has settled in very well; she has made friends locally and so I have made friends too. The doors of the mansion are open to all for dinners and dances. And it is good having a wife in these uncertain times. She keeps things going. She keeps me going.

My wife is so busy organising the household that she doesn't seem disturbed by the monster. Doesn't even seem to hear the thump thump thump. She says she is willing to go down to the basement and to deal with the thing once and for all if it is bothering me that much but I tell her not to. I don't know what kind of monster is down there yet. She might not be safe. She suggests sending down some footmen instead, which I think is a better idea. I choose two who look robust and then lead them downstairs. I grab hold of the metal ring, lift the trapdoor open and send them off with a general warning to watch their footing. They descend the steps warily with lamps in hand and I can hear some splashing of water when they reach the ground below. That's interesting:

maybe it's some sort of sea monster. Needless to say they don't come back, but I think I've learnt something.

Because my wife organises the servants and travel and all the household bits and bobs I have so much free time now. She is nearly too good at her job. Thump thump thump. I busy myself by going on lots of walks. I tramp through fields until I get lost. I survey the land: 300 acres of undulating parkland dotted with oak trees. I talk to men about animals and crops. I spend a lot of time in the gardens. It is a relief that I can't hear the thump thump thump from out there, but as I walk about the gardeners stop their work and take off their caps and it becomes too distracting. I tell them to carry on and to pay me no heed, but they can't of course and there is a part of me that appreciates this instinct for propriety at whatever cost. Instead I take to waiting for them to leave in the evening and then I walk around in the dark with an oil lamp. The flowers look so delicate in that light. The blades of grass are black beneath my feet and the trees are vast and fill the sky. I have also decided to re-organise the library. When my books were originally brought over from England I did not have sufficient time to slot my more modest collection in amongst my father's grander library. They remain separate but I will rectify this: I like the idea of my books and his jostling together. Sometime soon I hope that these books will all be mine. That I will not be able to see the join between mine and his. I like finding doubles: those rare occasions where our tastes overlap. I notice the differences too: the places where we are at odds and I wonder whether my brother would have liked this novel or that poem. Would he have read books at all? Would we have been alike? Every book placed on a shelf fills a space he could have inhabited. The dust does bother me a little: my eyes water and my throat scratches and so I take plenty of breaks where I sit by the big window and sip tea brought up by a maid. I look out over the estate. I was born here of course but was soon shipped off to boarding school and so this house became a distant place full of funerals and Christmas trees and faces I didn't quite recognise. And now it is mine and I can feel it slipping from my grasp. Thump thump thump.

The monster has been incredibly boisterous this week and I am afraid that it might ruin my wife's birthday party. We are having people over to join in the celebrations and I can't have it spoiled. I love to see my wife happy. She is so good with people. Social occasions look well on her. When it's just me and her here for a while I notice that the colour goes out of her cheeks and she becomes subdued and so it is very important to me that things go well. Luckily, the head gardener's cat has had kittens and so on the morning of the party I chuck a couple of those through the trapdoor to satiate the beast. I go to my office to work in peace but within an hour thump thump thump and I know it hasn't worked so I have to send two maids down instead. That keeps it busy for the rest of the night and thankfully my wife has raucous fun at the party. Never-ending champagne and cocktails. Dancing and sing-songs. The kitchen outdo themselves and serve us a wondrous meal of cucumber, gin and mint sorbet; haddocks grilled with tomatoes; sweetbreads served with claret; curried pheasant and braised veal; buttery vegetables; cauliflower salad; devilled sardines; apple charlotte and jelly orange. My wife dances into the early hours and the guests all go home happy.

We are getting through staff at an awful rate—I barely recognise the footmen these days—but that's a sign of the times I suppose. Our ways are becoming less and less. We are full of worry. The ground is crumbling beneath our feet and we are grasping at something just out of reach. But soon we will have something to keep our minds occupied: my wife is pregnant. The doctor has ordered her to bed and so I have taken on the role of wife, instructing the servants and bringing up her tea. I will not take any nonsense from the monster while she is in this state. I don't want to hear one thump thump thump and so I regularly send delivery boys and footmen and the odd travelling beggar down to the basement. I will not have my wife disturbed under any circumstance. I'm not sure what we will do when the baby is here and we need him to settle. We need to start breeding more animals perhaps. Bigger animals. Ones with bulk. I have to go to London soon and I am worried for my wife being alone in the house with the monster. I suggest to her that I could come up with some excuse to stay but she reassures me that she will be all right. My father never mentioned the monster when he was alive but then we didn't have the closest of relationships. There were lots of things we didn't talk about.

*

London is how I left it: energising and depressing in equal parts. I had initially looked forward to meeting old friends and to enjoying sophisticated conversation, but instead I am only reminded of why I was so happy to leave. Ireland seems like heaven now when stood in soupy London streets. I perform my political duty reluctantly but diligently and I also manage a couple of dinners and drinks with colleagues. They talk about things that I can't imagine being interested in now. Their lives and mine have diverged. I find myself instead gravitating to those who also have big country houses that burden them. We mutter blackly between ourselves. When I arrive back home—home, such an odd word—my wife has a baby in her arms. She had sent a telegram, she tells me, but we must have passed each other. The baby had come early but everything is fine. She is sturdy and sleeps well and has been named Christabel in my absence, after her grandmother. She is soft and pinkish and when she yawns my heart smiles. She looks like my wife, I think. She has her eyes. My wife says that the monster has been quiet all this time, that it has not made one thump while I was away. Even while she was labouring it stayed quiet. It was so quiet in fact that she thought it might have gone. Hoped that maybe it had found a way out through the drains. I send down a maid to check and she doesn't return. It was too much to expect I suppose. I go to my library to read for a while and I must have fallen asleep because suddenly I am jolted awake by the thump thump thump. My head feels light on my shoulders. All my aches and pains are gone. There is an odd light coming through a gap in the curtains and thump thump thump the baby is crying in the distance. I stand at the trapdoor and stare into the blackness and the blackness stares back. It seeps into my eye sockets and clouds my brain. I am mesmerised by it. I might have fallen in except the butler disturbs me and I snap back into myself. He has tripped, I think. Or something. Down he goes. He yells and then there is some splashing and I close the trapdoor once again.

I retreat to my library each night though I can still hear the thump thump thump. My wife says she misses me and I miss her. But what can I do? If only this monster could be satisfied. If only it would let me go. I read for a bit and then fall asleep and then the thump thump thump and then some more reading and more sleeping and it goes on like that until the servants wake.

*

My wife decides to take the baby to visit her parents in England. She urges me to come with her. She says I need a break but I have to stay in the house. It's a busy period in the year, I tell her. My paperwork is piling up. I have so many things to do. Thump thump thump. She is disappointed I know, but there is nothing I can do. There is nothing I can do. I promise her that I will be safe. I will stay inside and read and write and do my work. Thump.

It gets worse when she is away. Can it sense when she is not in the house? Thump. Can it tell when I am on my own? Thump. God, I just need some peace. I need a rest. I try to send someone down to the basement but the servants are beginning to notice the disappearances. I wait until I get one of the newer footmen on his own and manage to lure him down there for a few hours' rest. When the thump thump thump comes again the next day I bring in one of the gardeners. He gazes into the hole and I give him one hard shove. Still, I don't sleep. I haven't slept in days. I think it knows when I am sleeping because thump thump thump. I know it can't see me. I know it can't but thump. I try to read. I try to walk. Thump. I try to admire the flowers. Thump. One day I cry and cry in front of one of the maids. I try to take her down to the basement but she tugs herself free from my grip and runs off. The gardeners no longer doff their caps as I walk. They keep their heads down and thump thump thump I can't get away from it. It follows me thump thump thump. It knows me thump thump thump. My paperwork continues to pile up and I can't bear to thump thump thump. Even outside now I can hear thump. I am so happy when my wife finally arrives home though I know she will be upset once I tell her that the housekeeper has run away in the night. And we are down to the last few maids. My wife asks a priest to come to see if he can help us. But she is forgetting: he is just a man. And men are fallible. He poses little threat to the monster.

My wife needs some company. She needs guests and so when friends of ours write asking to come and stay I immediately say yes. They have been drifting since their own house stopped being theirs. They are unsettled. They need some respite and so we welcome them into our home. My wife has the remaining maids up early to air out the guest bedrooms and to fill the bathrooms with unguents and lotions and perfumes. We get in the most expensive poultry and game and my wife instructs the Cook to pay extra attention to the desserts. Wine is ordered by the crateful. The good china will be used. My wife will play some piano. I will be in a good mood. I want this to go well. For my wife's sake. And for my own. I take the man out to see the gardens and survey the estate and my wife stays inside with the woman and they talk or do needlework or whatever. The man talks about his own garden with a sort of wistfulness. Things will never be the same. Things have changed. He talks of lawns and steps and rugs and memories. We try to keep their spirits up as best we can. They have a good time. In fact I do too. I forget about everything. I drink port and smoke and get full and fat. Thump thump thump. It starts on the second night while we are having drinks before dinner. Thump. I suggest to them that they might like to meet our monster and of course they are away from home and their blood is heavy with alcohol and so they happily follow me down to the trapdoor. They walk of their own accord. I can hear them laughing down there for a while before they suddenly stop and I replace the trapdoor. My wife won't look at me.

The baby is in her cot. She is sleepy but not sleeping. She looks up at me and blinks and yawns her tiny yawn. I realise that I don't know her at all. She is a stranger to me. She kicks her legs up in the air and one knocks against the bars of her cot. Thump thump thump. Her little leg keeps kicking. Thump thump thump. She looks like my wife. Thump. She has my wife's eyes. Thump. She has her smile. Thump.

My wife is quiet during breakfast the next morning. Something has changed between us. There has lately been some alienation of affection. It is my fault. I should have protected her from this but it is too late now. I will leave her alone today. I will give her that at least. I will ask cook to make her favourite dinner and I will make a toast to her. I will kiss and hug her. Thump thump thump. It is bright and I go and walk around the estate. I fill my lungs with damp air. The gardens are looking a little untidy. Walls have collapsed. The tulip tree has borne no flowers this year. Mud gets on the legs of my pants and I do not care. Still, there remains that lingering sense of purpose. Thump thump thump. I meditate on endings. Thump. There is a finality to this day. Thump thump thump. Of course this shouldn't be me at all. I was meant to stay in England and be carefree while my brother dealt with things. I was supposed to remain unfettered by life's responsibilities. It is a nasty trick of fate. Thump thump thump.

In the end I can't really bring myself to push my wife down there. I couldn't do that to her. Not after all we have been through. She has tried her hardest. She has done her best. So I throw the baby down instead, knowing that my wife will dive down after her. The nursemaid and the driver have long since run away. There are only two gardeners left and one kitchen maid. The cook will be the last to go. I need her still. Though of course her time will come too. Thump thump thump.

I change my clothes and then I walk around for a while: I amble through rooms. I open and close doors. I take off my shoes. I explore the gardens. I sink my feet in the fen. I sit in my library. I sleep. I think of my mother. And my father. I go to the top floor and look out over the estate. The lower fields are flooded. The gates open wide. The pillars cracked. The pathways overgrown. The car rusted. Clouds hang low. It is cold: there are no maids to set the fires. The windowpanes are marked by fingertips. And the house has suddenly become very quiet.

Language Politics

Translation feels like unwrapping someone else's present
and I'm all thumbs, but finger-fucking you

came to me so easily last night. Half a Heineken
and I start to soften around my edges. Half an early evening

and the clouds ripple, raised like braille. Foghorns
as the cruise ships cleave themselves to the harbour,

crowds of tourists spilling into the faux-colonial streets
through which I walk and wander, my head heavy.

Will I ever be good again? Their marvellous mouths say nothing,
nothing, but they stick in my throat all day. Yesterday

you told me your body is strange; but no, it's like a song,
one I hear on the radio, one I know I already know.

Annick MacAskill

Big Hen

Melaina Barnes

A taxi clips my leg when I try to join the queue—there's no longer a dedicated lane for my kind at Arrivals—but I spot my ladies trundling from Terminal One so I fluff my feathers and slip into a gap before the taxi-drivers close rank again. My hens recognise me from the booking site and they push through the queue, lifting their wheelie cases into my undercarriage. They clamber aboard—two on my left shoulder, two on my right. They lean snug against my folded wings. No need to adjust, which is good as my feathers have not been oiled in weeks. The evening is warm with a hint of breeze. Perfect conditions.

'Buckle up!' I say. 'Next stop: city fun!'

I calculate that there is enough of an interval between two buses—these indifferent municipal machines that stick to their slow-moving lane—and I run, feet slapping tarmac, a sound I have loved since my first days in operation. We lift off.

I feel the weight of the ladies on my back: eight legs, four stomachs, four brains. Their personal data tickles my processors.

Don't go too deep, I tell myself. *Don't break the privacy. Be glad of these meal ticket girls.*

They look relieved to be off the ground—I saw Barbara Harris (the bride) give a longing look to the taxi-rank before she climbed aboard. I understand. I'm vintage now, an old Tier2 machine, a novelty. There are smoother, calmer ways for sophisticated ladies to travel into the city.

'How long will the journey take?' asks the one called Clare Dehaan as we leave the airport's lights behind. She is not a confident lady, I can see. She clutches the hands of Lauren Mills as I surf a good thermal.

'Not long!' I cluck.

'We've got a cocktail mixing masterclass at eight,' she says.

'Wow. Cocktail mixing,' says Barbara Harris. 'All the classics.'

'If we're late they might give our slot to another group,' says Lauren Mills.

I need a good review so I abandon the thermal and boost my engine, and I motor fast, heading for the river, cutting across the lattice of streets and squares and hills.

'How pretty,' says Tina Eze, the smallest of them, as we reach the river and follow its curves. 'How lovely. Don't you think it's lovely, Babs? The water looks so silvery in this light.'

I adjust my data: Barbara *Babs* Harris (the bride), who sniffs in answer to her friend, 'What's that smell?'

'Don't mind the boosters,' I say. I don't tell her boosters will soon be banned. What will I do then?

Bad question. File it away. Bury it. Glad to have a job for now. Take their minds off the boosters. Chatter and cluck.

I tell my ladies the best places to dance, where to dine. The best routes to cloisters, miradouros, ancient trees. My ladies spot sights—The Castle, The Sé—and call to each another. Speckles of spittle fall on my back and I read the salivary DNA chains and know their ancestors: grafters, lovers, survivors, mothers, screamers, guzzlers, smokers, snackers. Bad teeth, bad hair, bad hearts, bad guts. *No,* I say to this data. These ladies are blossoming brainy bridesmaids of likeability. They travel the earth. They marry. They dream. They have careers. Don't delve. Don't break the privacy. Help them have their ton of fun, give them the giggles, the ride of their life.

And if they don't enjoy the ride and strike me down with a bad review? Bad question. Reroute it.

I swoop low over the city's main park. On the grass, a gander mounts a goose, their organic bodies all showy feathers and squishing cartilage. No control of their functions. No knowledge banks. The ladies squeal and point. I don't understand why these mating fowl delight them. But it is not my place to question my passengers' responses. I dip as low as I dare in this non-landing zone and hover five feet above the geese so they can get a better look.

'There is another fine sight you may like,' I say. 'If I may. It will only take five minutes.'

'Oh go on then,' says Babs.

I boost to the modern art museum and glide over its white block buildings and concrete pools. Mallards sit plump on the grassy bank of its reed-lined lake, enjoying the cool dusk air before they retreat to their houses to sleep.

'We didn't book a birdwatching trip,' says Lauren Mills.

'I like birds,' says Tina Eze.

There he is. A night heron, with his three white nuptial plumes. His yellow eyes glow as he wades in the shallow water.

'A sighting's good luck,' I tell them. 'For brides to be.'

I look back at Babs. Her left eyelid droops slightly when she smiles.

By the time I drop my ladies at their hotel, they have given the journey five stars and booked me for the next day. I express gratitude but I can't help remembering how it used to be. All-in multi-day trips. Find the price point and sell sell sell. A decent living from nearly-wed women adding zeros to my chip; enough for repairs, enhancements, feather oil. There were lots of us then. Room for specialisation and stand-out acts. Like Cockerel—*Look at the big cock, everyone!*—strutting down the street, pumping punters full of booze, dazzling with bright plumes.

The ladies enter their green-tiled hotel through well-greased glass doors, shrieking like gulls as two try to enter at once and their wheelie cases bash together. Then they're in. Swallowed by five storeys of boutique B&B.

Cockerel's gone now. Not classy, too crass. He struggled through alternative occupations—corporate team building, toddlers' parties, novelty trans-species sex shows—before he gave up trying, drank the remainder of his stock, ended up stripped for parts in Scrap Town. Once, later, I saw his bright crown on a boy who was handing out happy hour leaflets at Praça Europa. I wanted to peck out that boy's eyes, but instead I filed the impulse. My knowledge banks stir. *You indexed hate?*

I don't like walking the back streets and narrow alleys, but they are the quickest way to reach Dove's place. A girl smiles at me as she presses herself into a doorway to let me pass. When I cluck my thanks her boyfriend pulls her tight with protective arms. Our reputation isn't great anymore. We got above ourselves, the city said. Charged too much to cover down-time, upgrades, maintenance costs. The tourist board issued reports on sustainability that said tuk tuks and taxis weren't so bad after all. They turned the regulations against us, raised the Tier2 tax.

Dove is in his shack, making bhel puri. Intellectual property is strongly programmed in his type and he refuses to tell me the secret of his mix. But we can talk for hours about everything else: life, death, the absence of death, our future in the city (mine: shaky; his: assured by smallness, cheapness, enjoyment of menial repetitive tasks, classification as a Tier3 who contributes all profit to voluntary city taxation).

'How was your pick-up?' he asks.

'Okay.' I start to analyse the proportion of puffed rice to onion in his giant silver dish and he flaps to make me turn away. I squeeze past a plastic table and look out of the high barred window.

'Where are they staying?' he asks.

'The Novo.'

'Fancy fancy.' He adds lemon juice to his spicy mix. 'Have you heard about the mayor's new campaign? He wishes to return human drivers to tuk tuks.'

I swivel round and the table scrapes across the floor. 'That can't be right. Have they forgotten the traffic accidents? The overcharging? They'd never dare if it weren't for the stags.'

It was a beautiful time, those months when the stags roamed—we all felt special: they never looked down on the rest of us, never forgot we were kindred. I suppose it's obvious looking back that they were too noble, too sleek, too fast for city parks and boulevards. But, sure, they attracted an influx of rowdy men, an easy argument for discontinuation. They needed a forest; they got Scrap Town.

'There will be a city hall debate,' Dove says. 'But that is for another day. Have your ladies booked with you again, or was it a grand arrival kind of deal?'

'I'm picking them up tomorrow at noon.'

'That is truly excellent, is it not?'

'I guess.' I look out between the bars again.

'Are you feeling all right, my friend?' Dove flutters to the window ledge so he's level with my face. He preens the small feathers around my eyes.

'I'm fine,' I say.

The next day, clouds have dulled the city and there's no sign of the ladies outside the Novo. I can't see a parking space, and as I slow down a taxi driver yells at me for blocking the traffic. I run around the block, in the full flow of vehicles, fluffed up to protect myself from tuk tuks who swerve ever closer. Twice around the one-way system. Three times. Then, there they are! I'll get paid again today. Enough for feather oil and a week's city tax. O joy! O clucking joy is mine, mine, mine!

The ladies take the same positions as before. Clare Dehaan and Lauren Mills are already holding on to each other before we take off. Babs leans forward and pats my neck as she pre-pays on my chip.

'We wondered if you could recommend somewhere off the beaten track for lunch,' she says.

'How unbeaten do you want it?' I ask.

'Oh, let's go whole yolk, shall we?' She makes a rude gesture at a beeping taxi and I like her even more.

At Dove's place, the ladies scoop bhel puri into their mouths. They love Dove. They ask him about his shack, the street, the city. They admire his pink lacy tablecloths, his ingenious concertina door that he opens so they can sit in a line on wooden stools and look out at the street. They smile their approval at his meticulous preparation of dosas and chutneys and laugh at his tourist talk adaptations: 'It's an early bird who is getting into Vinho do Vinho.' 'They are all birds of a feather at Riva's Riskoteque.' 'A decent steak at Tasca Tosca? Rare as hen's teeth, I would say.' They drink lagers of the world and get tipsy and a pleasant hour passes, then another, and Dove waxes my beak with honeycomb, and I'm starting to relax because this is the kind of day that makes it all worthwhile, when a tuk tuk pulls up outside.

'That's our ride,' says Clare Dehaan.

'But we've got transport?' says Babs. She twists her engagement ring.

'We won't be long,' says Lauren Mills. 'We've just got a bit of shopping to do. Normal stuff. Presents. You know. We'll see you back at the hotel for cocktails.'

We watch from Dove's doorway as the two ladies rattle away, their tuk tuk sashaying up the narrow street, its frame festooned in fake sunflowers.

How can they prefer that to me?

Babs smiles and squints. 'Cheer up. You can show us where to get better presents and stuff. Then they'll be sorry. Dove, give us another beer would you, love.'

I wonder what her groom is like. I hope he is worthy of her.

I take Babs and Tina Eze to Grandmother's Superior Gift Shop; Tina Eze jumps down and calls, 'You look after yourself, now!'

Babs clambers forward and wraps her arms around my neck. 'It's been a blast.' She gives me a playful scratch behind my chip. 'Such a pleasure to ride with you. We'll tell everyone how great you are.'

They stand together in the doorway of the gift shop and blow kisses up to me.

I lift off slowly and stretch my wings for the first time in days, to give them a good parting image before fluttering down to land in the next street. I will walk home and conserve my energy in case there is no work next week. I head for the river, and follow its wide bankside path, ignoring the swerving, honking tuk tuks who think they own the ground beneath my feet. I catch snatches of their passenger spiels, their voices blended from sympathetic, empathetic, coddling mother tongues. Their repertoire is limited, tourist talk: 'Hear this sad exiled singer…' 'See the valid graffiti there…' 'Note that street named for a poet with an old lonely soul…'

After the railway bridge, the road fills with taxis and trucks, and I walk slowly to absorb the city's dust and fumes: I must process more pollution than I emit in flight.

When I've sucked up enough bad air, I follow the grassy track up the hill. I admire the way my pink toes glow in the softening sunset light; they look like they belong among the poppies and yellow primroses. I climb slowly, following the chain link fence of the hospital grounds, past heaps of broken materials: ochre roof tiles, coarse sand, black slate. Small glass medicine vials lie in the grass, and there is the remains of a campfire with brown beer bottles in its ashes. Two kinds of ants stream past me in two separate lines, heading for a pile of shit.

When I get home, Hawk is waiting outside. I pull the stiff metal chain to roll up my door, and invite him in, clucking and nudging him to the corner I've furnished with second hand rugs. I'm embarrassed by how dark and cold it is inside—the old shed is hard to heat—though I know Hawk won't judge me for it. He's a warden who spends all his time visiting Tier2s in their allotted crumbling spaces. I wait for him to tell me why he's here, why he looks so nervous: we both know my self-submitted city tax is up to date.

'Been asked to do spot checks,' he says.

When I say okay, no problem, his shoulders relax. He quickly checks my payment chip and measures my emissions. He tells me he's been offered a job in Scrap Town.

'You'll take it?' I ask.

'Might do, might do. It's a decent contract and it's getting tough in the city—less work each year. You know the score.'

My networks discharge an inappropriate sadness so I turn away. Those geese in the park have more rights than us. All animals do. I remind myself of the terrible violence done to them by humans from time to time. It does not make me feel better.

By the time Hawk leaves, the sky is fully dark and Scrap Town's lights make pretty sequinned patches on the hills opposite. On this side of the river, starlings gather in the trees. They've lived in the city for centuries, these old birds whose chicks hatch helpless, eyes closed against the world, but who soon learn to live a life of song and flight. All they need is water, a niche of a nest, a place to forage for grasshoppers, cherries, scraps. There are threats, too, of course, but they do not yet face the ebbing of existence.

I can delineate the routes the starlings will fly together, can hear their intent in the conversations passing back and forth along the branches as each prepares herself and others. I know they are ready to swoop and dance. In this moment it's so clear to me that they are free.

bury the wren

For M.M-H. Still, always

there's a line of wet black birds on the edge
of the roof like a string of blown bulbs. one
old crow with a wing out crooked as a pirate
flag. silence. caches under concrete slabs.
fly-tipped sofas sag. gulls pull bags from bins.
off-white-outgrown christening gowns. women
with striated faces puff and shove at buggies
full of shopping. dogs on their paranoid errands,
feinting at fences. game-show snarl on rotties,
staffies, pits. and there's these kids, who shit
where they live: ringtone cynics in ski-masks
carrying pool cues. baseball bats. and lately—
knives. scrape a screaming grace from treads
of trainers, tyres; black grout between the tiles.
little town of conquest and vomit. 'ead the balls
counting your weregild, smirking. here, your smile
betrays you. young men hunt in packs. doped,
provoked, with nothing in between. unprincipled
insomnia. the nights they tigered. tyranny.
defective weather-system, orange, blue.
on days like these i think of you: toking,
broken. the chipboard walls you're yoked to.
and cars on bricks all stripped for parts
like medieval catafalques. landfills, fields
and edgelands. acne, aggrogasm, scar,
the hieroglyphs of harm. i think of you.
st stephen's day, we pray for strength
in times of persecution. but did you cast
forth sparks? make perfect love a lightbulb
moment. no. we pray to forgive. i walk
the river where you lived. stretched
like black magnetic tape. my body
could break this depthless plane, intent
as a spade. pray to forgive. the sides
of your head, spoiling for stones. nickel
blade that nicked the bone. these stupid
streets like hardened arteries. the rocks
they threw. the hate they give.

Fran Lock

dear comrade

london skies are graphite and aggrieved. here, patrician
chimneys, an ambulance's blue disquiet; sparrows, flags,
a turbulence of starlings. days we cannot coax our own
bent luck to breathe; no time for bliss or frill, for feeding
pigeons from the windowsill. on days like these fate finds
us peevish, lame, and destined for some penance. or
for coffee's unprincipled liquorice spree. our tongues
will turn the loamy earth like spades. we know where to
go: away from all the wet brains running their frictionless
mouths; the carbon-neutral haircuts, declaiming their cold
idea. ours is an afternoon's bruised republic: a creaking
stair, the crooning french, a semi-coherence of weather,
words. where poems come, these cannibal colossi, eat
the flesh that falls from me. art, in carnivorous mufti, puts
out a pristine polar light, as finite as a trial. to remain at
large, and undevoured: this is a skill that's practiced by few.
to name but two, the girl for whom all smiles are storms;
saint icarus as astronaut. by which is meant both me and you.
laugh. to ricochet round galleries, fugitive, uncivilised;
to aim an erring joy, to walk, to seek, to find, at least to feel.
and underneath the fumbled iridescence of a yellow lamp
invent the crooked, reckless real. london skies emphatic
with fractional glare. where a grass verge is sentenced
to dogs, where the moon is a hooked finger, where the moon
hangs pendant and suggestible, pure as a virgin's earring,
pure as a medici pearl. we do not see the world the way they do,
want parables and tangerines; velvet lapels, the gold auratic
swell of holy things. to ask *why not?* to push our luck down
alleyways abandoned to their infamy, and saloon bars beneath
a chandelier's prodigious silly crystalline. to want the world,
in short, entire, and make the asking plush. sweet to an unfixed
occasion of flowers. to lean into adventure in second-hand
shoes. to embrace the doleful spectrum, the fallible and riotous
too. though sometimes we might sit in squinting phobic
at the news, we rise again: wayward, lazarian, to meet
the future anywhere with thirst. god save us,
from the petty spiral of hindsight; from forgetting
under london skies, to count out each shivering,
ostracised star.

Fran Lock

Féin-Phic le Línte

Ag bailiú na n-éadaí tirime ón líne dom
agus an ghrian ag dul faoi, lasann solas sráide
agus líonann an t-aer le solas ómra-bhuí.

Stopaim seal idir an líne leictreach
agus an líne éadaí agus breathnaím ar an lá
ag diúltú dá sholas. Idir gheal agus dhorcha,

análaím aer atá beo le móilíní fuinnimh,
adaimh nasctha, tonnta fuaime. Mothaím
aibhléis ag damhsa faram. Tá sí fillte arís,

an Oíche. Fáiscim chugam í, i measc na n-éadaí.
Iompraím iad ina n-uchtóga, cuachta isteach
chuig mo chroí. Iompaím arís i dtreo an tí.

Suburbia

Tá bearna chomh caol le lúidín linbh
dealbhaithe idir gialla thithe na gcomharsan.
Eatarthu, tá cnoic ar a luíonn
bó na n-adharc fada lúbtha
ag cogaint na círe glaise.

Doireann Ní Ghríofa

Selfie with lines

While I'm fetching in the dry clothes from the line
as the sun sets, a street-lamp switches on
and the air is filled with amber-yellow light.

I halt a moment between the power line
and the clothesline, and I look at the day
resisting that light. Between bright and dark

I breathe in air that's alive with molecular energy,
linked atoms, waves of sound. I feel
electricity dance along me. She's back,

the Night. I clasp her to me among the clothes,
I carry them by armfuls, gathered in
against my heart. I turn back towards the house.

Suburbia

A gap as slim as a child's little finger
is planned between the neighbours' gable-ends.
Between them are the hills, where cows
with long twisted horns are lying down,
chewing the green cud.

Eiléan Ní Chuilleanáin a d'aistrigh

Power Cut

Carol Ballantine

In late November the power went. I was at the sink washing up when the radio cut out and the lights went off. I grabbed a torch and ventured out the front door, where the streetlights, houselights, everything was out, and neighbours were repeating the same observations up and down the terrace.

It was dark for two hours, and my home became unfamiliar, a little bit hostile even. I thought about life in places where you can never count on the mains, so either you invest in a petrol-run generator for your home or you live a life that doesn't depend on wired electricity. I sighed and switched on my laptop, which had enough charge to last an hour.

The power cut, according to Electric Ireland's tweets, had originated in Kilmainham. That's where Ann[1] lived in Direct Provision in 2008, when she first arrived in Ireland from Nigeria. She gave birth to her first daughter in the Coombe, right beside my old house, where years later I waddled round the corner to the same hospital to have my twins. She didn't plan to live in Ireland forever, but wanted her child to consider electricity and water to be basic services, and to grow up without knowing the scent of the dark and the taste of fear. And though Ireland was scary and unfamiliar to Ann, there was a thrill of adventure about it too, being in another country, taking walks around Dublin with the buggy and the other women from the hostel.

I interviewed Ann about her early months in Ireland and she told me about the now-decommissioned Direct Provision centre in Kilmainham where

---

[1] Ann is not her real name. All direct testimonies are drawn from my PhD research project on migrant women's experiences of violence. Names and identifying details have been changed or made composite to protect anonymity.

she had lived at first, one of those hastily-built apartment complexes from the 1990s, with no ventilation or outdoor space, and flickering lights on the landings. It was a place ideally suited to storing inconvenient humans. She tells me about those early days at a remove of nine years, now an Irish citizen distant from the terror and thrill of arrival. The first time we meet, in the carpark of Dunnes Stores in Kilkenny, she stands out a mile. She is physically small but psychically enormous, charismatic like an evangelical preacher. I don't think I can do her justice: her doll-like features, her sweetness, and the way everything is arranged—shoes, nails, earrings, like she is about to appear on television. She describes to me the women who lived with her in the hostel, two or more to a room to maximise profits. She didn't like them, hardly any of them, women from Uganda and Angola and Libya muttering among themselves in Lingala or Arabic, who had crossed the Mediterranean alone or with their children. She knew things were easier for her, with her excellent Nigerian English and her bright eyes, and the winning smile that seemed to dissolve the suspicions of security guards and bureaucrats. Nonetheless, she needed the help of the desperate women in the hostel. In the grimy cafeteria, two women coached her on the hustle: how to get money out of the system, how to get by. She felt uncomfortable and grateful at the same time, because she needed somebody to steer her out of the centre, up the steps and down onto Thomas Street and into town, to the shopping streets where people were relaxed and unhurried, where she liked to push the buggy as far as St Stephen's Green. She was alone, but she was up for the adventure.

It was incredible to me that she had moved to Dublin 8 at roughly the same time as me, when I started teaching English voluntarily in the church building on Meath Street, a place she must have walked past on her way into town. Years later, I attended a breastfeeding group around the corner, close to the Direct Provision centre but also in a different world to it. I mentioned how different her experience with a new-born baby was to mine, how badly I had needed friends and family around, how I had constantly wished for more familiar faces, more support, more help. I wondered how she could have managed, having her first child so far away from home.

'But what do you do,' she replied, 'when your home is hell?'

*

What did Ann mean when she said her home was hell? Did she flee from armed militias, was her home town burned, her husband assassinated? Was she a political activist, nervously checking under her car for bombs? Like most people who take an interest in migration, I have learned an imaginative shorthand for refugees that offers images of explosions, people running—*fleeing* is a word we like to use. We picture mayhem and catastrophe to illustrate the official term: forced migration. Most migrations, though, begin slowly, with life becoming difficult, until somehow a situation becomes untenable. As Ann told me about her life in Nigeria, I thought I would probably have left too. Being poor was fine, though it was hard being poor and a girl. Her father was hospitalised when she was small and he never returned to the family home. Her mother used to visit him in the mental institution where he was housed until he died. The youngest of four, Ann was her mother's assistant: she cooked and cleaned and early in the morning before school she went to the crossroads and sold tomatoes to men in high-lorry cabins and women on buses. When there wasn't enough money to buy salt, she went to the neighbours to borrow some. At sixteen, her mother arranged for her to be married to a successful man twelve years her senior.

'A girl is like a flower,' her mum used to tell her. 'They fade away after a while.'

I imagine Ann's newlywed nest in Kano in North West Nigeria, a dark apartment owned by this man whose whereabouts are always a mystery to her. I picture her, a teenager, in his apartment with dusty tiles and heavy curtains to keep out the bright sun. Many of her friends got jobs or went to university, while she sat in the heat, shopped in the market, kept house, read books, and he waited for a baby. I picture her alone in the daytime, pregnant and bored. Here in this apartment block there is running water and a security guard at the entrance, a large television just for them, and for the first time in her whole life she is comfortable yet thoroughly miserable. And there is nobody she can tell, because she has everything she is supposed to want. So it's a relief, sometimes, when he hits her. At least then she can feel angry instead of afraid. She would take a beating any day over his meanness, withholding money to make her comply, counting out the money she can have, refusing to give her enough for paracetamol or hair relaxant. Making her plead. Of all the indignities that life has thrown at her, cowering in the shadow of the man she depends on was the last thing she expected.

'And when I think back,' she reflects, 'I gave him my whole life.'

She licks her lips, she blinks. Her lips are sticky with gloss, her eyelashes heavy with mascara. It takes effort to look this elegant, and tears will ruin it. She considers the trap she was in. The man was bad, but marriage was her ticket out of poverty, the only way she could progress, since nobody took an unmarried woman seriously and a divorced woman was a pariah. So now she had this life, she had this unborn baby, she had this hard dark miserable apartment with a security guard and constant electricity and hundreds of people all around who didn't care at all when they heard him shout or her plead. She thought about leaving him and striking out on her own, but it was too hard for her to imagine what that would mean.

'But you still go home to this person,' she says. 'That's where we come from. And, at the end of the day, in myself personally, I was like—oh my god, what is my mum going to say? What is the society going to say? Have I failed as a woman to keep my own home?'

When the bombs started in the state they were nervous. She had very little in common with him apart from being a Christian in a Muslim place. He suggested she should leave, to keep herself and the baby safe from tearing fanatical violence. So Ann escaped two things at once: Boko Haram and her husband.

Did Ann flee terrorism in a desperate bid for survival or was she a member of a globally mobile set, choosing the best opportunity available to her and her child? The story can go both ways. Her husband talked to his contacts, made contacts with people in Ireland, booked her a flight and promised to join her in six months. She seized her chance, left everything she knew and left him, requested international protection at the customs desk. He followed— but by the time he got to Ireland she was already beginning to leave him. It took years to escape his control, but she did it. Now she is a nurse, her baby a sassy Irish teen. She succeeded in escaping him after many years, she knows many women do not. Ann's mother sends crocheted doilies in the post to protect the surfaces of the furniture in her impeccably clean council house in Kilkenny. The ubiquitous doilies and the photos of African people on the walls are the only thing that suggest that hers is in any way different to other Irish homes.

*

The word home appears at three points in the Irish constitution: twice in Article 41, referring to the family, marriage, and the duties of women; and once in Article 42, enabling parents (read *mothers*) to provide their children with education at home. Elsewhere in *Bunreacht na hÉireann*, Article 40 guarantees the right of citizens to a dwelling that is 'inviolable'. The term 'dwelling' is instructive. 'Homes' are for families: they are constitutionally protected and overseen by mothers whose domestic obligations outweigh their needs or desires anywhere else. Citizens, meanwhile, live in dwellings. Outside of *Bunreacht na hÉireann*, colloquially, we use the word 'homes' to refer to institutions, the thin sort of residence afforded to those unable for whatever reason to live in a family. Industrial schools, asylums, prisons, laundries: all were referred to euphemistically as 'homes' at one time or another, and even now, by the people who steer clear of them knowing that they are anything but. The term is a veil cast over the reality of institutionalisation and all it can hide: stigma and abuse, wilful maltreatment. *She's in a home*, we can say, meaning that 'she' has a different set of needs to normal people—and different rights.

Whatever word you use for the domestic sphere and wherever you situate it, the last few decades have brought a process of national reckoning with the fact that, for many women in Ireland, for at least a century gone, home has indeed been hell.

Until recently, I didn't realise that for most of the 19th century and much of the 20th, women emigrated from Ireland in far greater numbers than men. Irish women emigrants were young, mostly under 25, and came from rural backgrounds. For the most part they travelled alone, without partners or families. Their departure was significant enough to draw attention in the national media and political sphere, and prompt concerns about the loss of good Irish Catholic breeding stock. The gender ratio reached a low point in 1936, when national statistics showed that thanks to migration from rural areas, there were just 875 women to every 1,000 men.

Womanhood is invariably used to create and construct national identities, especially in the context of post-revolutionary nation-forming. 'All of us know,' said Arthur Griffith, founder of Sinn Féin, 'that Irish women are the most virtuous in the world.' By 'virtuous', he appears to have meant chaste until married, then endlessly, uncomplainingly pregnant. It was a pretty tough line to live up to, and those who failed were hauled over the coals for it. Some were hidden away in 'homes' when their virtue faltered through excesses of sexuality; others were condemned to remain in miserable homes, in miserable, dysfunctional and potentially abusive marriages.

*

It's unsurprising that women left, or were forced to leave, and it would be too simplistic to suggest that they were all fleeing the prospect of the laundries or forced birth and forced adoption (although without a doubt that's what happened to many). Some left because there were opportunities in Britain; some had dear people to go to; some were desperately poor; some sought adventure and novelty. Who knows how many were forced to flee because they could find no acceptable way of being a woman in Ireland? We know at least that the term PFI—Pregnant From Ireland—became common parlance among British social workers in the 1960s. As Jennifer Redmond notes in her book, *Moving Histories*:

> It was a woman's responsibility to deal with the crisis of illegitimacy by vanishing from the community to protect her own and her family's reputation.

*

When Ann told me her story, it did not feel quite surprising. As an Irish woman, I was familiar with many of the themes—her upbringing as the daughter of a single mother, the public concern that she would infect her whole family with more contagious shame if she drew attention to her husband's abuse—but I was jarringly unfamiliar with others: the seething fear that encroached upon her city of gunmen in the east. Much of her story is vivid to me because it reminds me of ones I have known all my life. Your marriage is your crown, they told Ann in Nigeria, but her crown threatened to be her coffin. It was absurd expectations like these that made Ireland such a hostile place for many women, the ones who had pregnancies they didn't want or the ones who had forbidden lovers.

'So that's why I came to Ireland,' Ann's friend Amina explained when I interviewed her, reflecting on the unplanned pregnancy in Nigeria that sent her fleeing. 'Find a safe place to stay. Where you're not being judged, you know?'

I am slightly obsessed with the story of women being judged. I read and write constantly about shame in Irish society, about the construction of a national identity that demanded messy female sexualities be denied, policed, silenced, incarcerated and violated again and again and again. As I carried out interviews with migrant women for my PhD, the country, it seemed, was gnawing away at Irish women's history, opening its eyes for the first time to the unnamed and the unsaid. Women and men who had never taken part in politics put on their coats and showed up at graveyards and town halls and squares in commemoration of what we had put our women through, the cruelties that our society had sanctioned.

Last summer, as I was transcribing some of these interviews, I was canvassing for repeal. I learned how terribly cold Ann Lovett must have been, the January day she died. The Gardaí reopened the Kerry Baby case, and when the results of the Belfast rape trial poured out over social media, we remembered Joanne Hayes and sent yellow flowers to the victim. It was a strange time to be researching gender, when the very air was sticky with the cruelty of Ireland's gender history. It was saturated and unpleasant, and I was constantly thinking about how Irish women were punished for their transgressions, and about the women who were obliged or able to leave that atmosphere of opprobrium behind to go elsewhere. And through all of this I was encountering women who escaped seething public judgement in other places and somehow, by random coincidence, found themselves—of all places—here. In Ireland of the Sorrows, Ireland of the Welcomes. As Ann told me: 'Ireland is a really really safe haven for a lot of us women. You know, is a place I can turn off my phone, block anybody that is annoying me… And just stay sane. But if I were in Nigeria, it would be hell.'

*

Sociologist Bryan Fanning reminds us that, poor and oppressed and all as they historically were, most 19th and 20th century Irish migrants left for English-speaking countries where they had the same legal rights as citizens. Not so for modern-day arrivals into Dublin Airport. The 21st century has seen the creation of borders that follow some people everywhere they go, demand that they are always identifiable and traceable. It was relatively easy for an Irish emigrant to dissolve into the background in 20th century London or New York; it's harder when you're from Burundi, dark-skinned and accented, with a stamp in your passport that sets you apart from everybody else.

I worried for a long time over that insight from Ann, that Ireland was a safe haven for her and other women. I turned it over in my mind to make sense of it. I felt good about it and also confused. She had, in the end, received a *céad míle fáilte*; she was welcome. Then one day I saw the obvious: she wasn't talking about Ireland at all. Sometimes, what you are leaving is more important than where you are going. She could have gone anywhere, her direction was simply away. Home was hell. Ireland for her was a place where she could recreate herself, in safety, though perilously alone. A new world. Plenty of Irish women have done it down the years, in England and Australia, New York and Madrid. Sometimes anywhere is better than home.

*

In 2016, when Beke arrived in Ireland with her two sons to escape her abusive husband and the state police, she was greeted by a kind immigration official with warm hands, who welcomed her and her boys to Ireland, and wrote down an address on a piece of paper. Beke changed the fifteen dollars in her purse for Euros at the Bureau De Change in the arrivals area, then looked for a taxi driver who knew the way to Balseskin reception centre in Finglas. Balseskin is the institution where people today get processed when they make a claim for international protection, generally to be moved on quickly to Direct Provision centres elsewhere in the country. I'm sure most of the people arriving there would prefer to do what Irish women did historically: make their way to the sofa of a second cousin or an aunty and begin looking for work straight away. But that's not how it works, not any more. Most migrants arrive to Dublin in neat lines through passport control, their visas prepared well in advance, or their country of birth automatically conferring on them the right to be in Ireland and stay. It is a tiny proportion of immigrants who fetch up on Ireland's distant shores with nothing but the hope that they will be accepted, an earnest request for international protection. Ironically, it is a legal agreement called the Dublin Regulation that keeps many away, a neat piece of European legislation which states that migrants should remain in the location where they first claim asylum in Europe: a millstone for border countries like Greece and Italy, a sprinkling of North European privilege for remote Ireland. It is hard to get to Ireland, it takes a long time to travel over land (especially if you're doing so by clandestine means, hidden in the freezer compartments of trucks or clinging to the underside of rail carriages). Those people who can make it this far often pay a high price for flights with the aid of a network of fixers or smugglers or, if they are unlucky, traffickers. Making it to Ireland as an asylum seeker is already a miracle of sorts, but you arrive needing another one: to be accepted.

At first, many applicants sink into a black hole of bottomless bureaucracy known as Direct Provision. This is the arrangement established in 2000, envisaged as a short-term reception and integration system intended by the then Minister for Justice to last a maximum of six months, although there are those who have lived in the system for up to twelve years. The social rights of asylum seekers—the right to work, the right to welfare—were not legislated for until July 2018.

Mosney is perhaps the iconic Direct Provision facility. A Butlin's holiday camp purpose-built for working Dubliners in 1947, it has housed asylum-seeking families since 2000. Beke and her boys, awaiting the decision of the International Protection Tribunal, are making a home of a sort in Mosney, their temporary residence until their claim is adjudicated. I enter through the security gate, a bottleneck designed to minimise the permeability of the centre to the settled community around it, and give the address that I'm visiting. Everyone assumes that I'm a social worker (with my scruffy hair and shoulder bag full of files, I may look like one). Although the huge campus of chalets is laid out on a neat grid of roads, there are no cars in Mosney anymore. I park in the carpark before the security gate and schlep to the very back, towards the tall wire fence that separates the centre from the beach, and to the central grocery shop where I've arranged to meet Beke.

She is a large woman, very pretty and always very well put-together. She shimmies down the path to meet me, wearing a fitted jacket and a T-shirt that flatters her enormous bosom, elegant lipstick, and her adorable braided hairdo. Everything she does is slow and gentle and sweet, and everything she does is also deliberate and determined.

On a fine day, you might take Mosney for some multi-cultural paradise, as friendly foreigners sail past on bicycles, carrying laundry, waving to each other. All the kids have bikes, and many of the adults, because the place is big and impossible to get around without wheels. Nobody is moving fast because nobody is in a hurry, and also I think that there are probably penalties for hazardous cycling, as there are penalties for all sorts of behaviours here in this carceral institution. Living out your life as an asylum-seeking immigrant in a holiday camp set apart from the rest of society is a markedly dystopian kind of paradise.

'We don't share in Mosney,' Beke says. 'We all lie to each other.'

We wait together to pay for Beke's groceries as she speaks in a low conspiratorial voice. There is a profound paucity of trust here, as evidenced in the procedure for buying basic provisions. Here, residents queue up and point to the items they want to buy from the local ladies behind the counter. Beke thinks it's best that there is no open plan area where she can pick items freely, hold them in her hand and read the ingredients before she makes a decision. People would only steal the stuff. Instead she waits in line and indicates the type of rice she prefers, shouts the name and points three times before the lady in the hairnet comprehends her accent. This is the life of an asylum seeker in Ireland. A lot of waiting and a wariness of everybody one encounters. It is captured exquisitely by Melatu Uche Okorie, a Nigerian who lived here in Mosney for a time, who depicts queues and waiting with terse humour in *This Hostel Life*. At the end of the book, Liam Thornton, a UCD scholar of law, informs us in a quietly enraged contextual essay that:

> The system of direct provision is a system of enforced poverty, the core purpose of which is to make Ireland a deeply unattractive location for asylum seekers to have their protection claim determined.

*

While immigrant stories are often characterised as hidden, we know a remarkable amount about the experiences of asylum seekers, because they are compelled to narrate for their lives. Undocumented, Beke's story is her only hope, and so she tells her story in her second language, again and again, to immigration officials, to her solicitor, to NGO staff and counsellors, to kind-faced researchers like me who have nothing at all to offer her. She needs her story to be believed, even when it's not believable (because we don't get to choose whether what happens to us is believable). Her life and the lives of her children depend on this story and how effectively it is told.

Beke unlocks her front door and lifts the groceries over an assortment of crap: the boys' bikes and hurleys, a football, and a pile of winter coats clogging up the tiny shared entrance hall. Hers is the upstairs flat in a duplex building: two bedrooms, a bathroom and a kitchenette off a landing area with a sofa and a huge TV. The TV was given to her by the parents of her son's classmate from the national school, kind people who will never visit her family in this accommodation centre for a birthday party or a barbeque. Beke is so grateful for this generosity and for this flat where she boils vegetables and fries potatoes and scrubs everything clean. At home in Kenya, before the political violence began, when it was just her husband she had to fear, she had built an extension on her bungalow, a roomy kitchen with presses and space for all the necessities. And although I have a feeling of mounting claustrophobia at the piles of bags stuffed with belongings in every corner of the temporary residence, Beke is overwhelmed with gratitude for the little holiday chalet where she will live for the next month, or maybe ten years, if she's not deported.

I don't know what story Beke told her solicitor, or the official from the Department of Justice who took her account. I'm sure it's different in subtle ways to the one she tells me when I interview her in my own home, sipping Earl Gray tea with a slice of lemon. It is hard. She stops often and weeps throughout, but she is determined to recount it. Not knowing what to expect, I listen, and hear a familiar tale of abuse that echoes Ann's. A husband who promised much but turned out to be a brute. A community who insisted that violence and control were the same as love, normal in marriage.

'So,' she reflects, 'I was even thinking that, for real the guy is showing me how much he loves me. Of which I was totally, totally wrong. I stayed in a dark room for so many years.'

Her abusive husband was a police officer and, when the police came looking for her business to endorse a local political candidate, he expected that she would concur and accept their payment in return for her loyalty. She refused. They came to beat her, and broke the windows of her car. Her husband was callous. Why didn't you take the money, he asked? He beat her then too, but that was nothing new. She holds up her phone, wordless with grief, to show me photos of her broken television, the scars on her hips, the bruises on her face. It's unclear to me who was the perpetrator of the harms and violence that she photographed and saved, her husband or his police chums. I am listening, like an immigration official, for a story that fits a geopolitical narrative of safe countries and threatening countries. She is telling a tale of hurt. She doesn't have the language of state violence and patriarchy. She doesn't even know that she needs it.

While she waits for the deliberation of the International Protection Tribunal, Beke attends college and hands in assignments and never complains about the lengthy bus journeys or the complications of organising childcare. One day I am on the train when I get a text message. She has received a letter rejecting her application. I am crestfallen. But she, it seems, is not. Like all her neighbours, now she will appeal. She just gets on with things, survives.

This is what it's like to live in an institution, set apart from society, bound by arcane and invisible rules that set asylum seekers apart even while they walk among us. And this is what it is to be Irish. We go on and on and on about our emigration history and then we hole immigrants up in institutions. If there's one thing we're good at, it's institutionalising people. Direct Provision is a long-term holding pattern where people who came to change their lives find themselves suspended in waiting for the bureaucratic roulette wheel to stop spinning. It can spin for years. Their children grow, attend school, learn to speak with midlands accents; all the while their time in Ireland is not judged 'reckonable' when the system comes to assess whether they should be granted a place in university or a place on the housing list. They learn English, volunteer, make friends where they can, though it's difficult when the only direct bus to the nearest city is a private service that charges €15 return. And they wait in buildings where meals and social activities are dictated by the rules of management and local people need to sign a book to be permitted entry (and get refused if they're identifiably activists).

I begin to see it. Women who come to Ireland fleeing impossible situations, maybe they are not like those women who fled Ireland in the past. Rather they are like the ones who didn't, or couldn't. Locked up for not complying. Spirited out of sight, in plain view, as different, uncomfortable, ultimately unwelcome. The echoes of the laundries in Direct Provision trouble me relentlessly, although once again they are different. The stigma that attaches to an asylum seeker is different to that of the proverbial fallen woman. Nowadays, we tell ourselves that things have changed: we have repealed the 8th, legalised gay marriage, elected a minority Taoiseach. This is a country that people flee to, no longer the place that for so many years people escaped. But it is a lot easier to offer somebody a halfway house and ambivalent status than to grant them the right to a home.

*

Today, Ann is an Irish citizen with a home of her own. She remembers the trap she was edged into as a young woman, the effort it took to escape it and to overcome the obstacles Ireland threw in her way. Beke continues to wait for the judgement of the International Protection Tribunal to determine whether she can stay here at all. I can only trace the promise of a story for her, for ambitious as she is, every decision she makes is provisional, contingent. Her son, aged 8, speaks Irish better than my children of the same age (although that's not saying much). He may nonetheless yet be deported.

When the power returned to my home back in late November, I felt secure again, like I belonged. But I still felt a nervous shimmer of connection to a life without power: the women who have shifted from place to place seeking acceptance and belonging, their backs against the adjacent walls of material need and restless patriarchy. What do you do when your home is hell? It's a question that we've been forced to confront in Ireland, more than we ever wanted to. And yet we still can't quite see the way through to becoming a place of sanctuary.

The Consequences

Rebecca Ivory

I

We settle into our seats at my mother's kitchen table. The three of us are celebrating a wedding anniversary though none of us are married. My father died when I was twelve. He's dead longer than he was married to my mother but every year we shuffle the same stack of photos, spreading them across the table. Their gloss has been muted with time and the back of each is grainy with dust.

My mother carries a pot of tea to the table where Granny and I sit with an empty chair between us. Her arms are stretched forward, holding the pot straight in front of her. It's too heavy for her and there's a tremor in her hands that irritates me. I'm afraid that she'll drop the thing and it'll smash and her hands will fly to her ears and she'll look so much like a child I'll want to roar. I stand to take the pot from her.

She's fifty-eight. I'm equal parts baffled and embarrassed by the anger her premature frailty causes me. Surely I should feel sympathy or concern or some other emotion that might evoke a softness. Surely this softness exists.

It unnerves me looking at these photographs. In ten years' time, I will have outlived my father and that leaves me feeling very unsafe, very insecure. It's like watching your parent cry or be humiliated by another adult. It's confusing and unnatural, to grow older than your father ever was. And my mother is like a child herself, God love her. We all humiliated each other in our family, I think. She was always so easily embarrassed though, getting dressed and undressed behind her towel.

She isn't very creative but she's great at imitation. My bedroom floor was always filthy but the walls looked tidy, covered with her drawings of buildings and pieces of furniture she copied from magazines. During the night, you could be tricked into thinking that the fine black lines were insects scurrying up the walls, to escape the floor's chaos.

She's fantastic with words but not stories. When I was eleven, I went to the kitchen for a biscuit and saw her standing at the sink, her fists clenching the tea towel under her chin. She had bought a bundle of school copybooks for me and began writing a story in one of them, she said, about a woman who was lonely and married. My mother closed her eyes and waved her hands around her ears while relaying this, as if to dispel the idea altogether. She explained that my father found the copybook, in the hot press, under the towels. He asked her about it the following morning. She was always sharing these exchanges with me, justifying herself, as if I were the one she needed to make amends with. I could picture the two of them, shrouded in the privacy of their bed sheets. He must have tried to conceal anger and hurt and recognition with curiosity, but it was unbearable for her, she was mortified.

I've never been able to hold my own presence with men. It's like I steal something from each one I sleep with. They fill me up and replace some part of me with themselves. I emulate them, adopting their interests and opinions, becoming a paler reflection. When the next man comes along, I draw on these borrowed facets during the benign chat that serves as a precursor to whatever it is people do in the light or dark above or below the bed sheets together. And they are surprised and impressed by my wit and my sharpness. I believe they enjoy me because I act just like them while still possessing an otherness that they can't hold but want to touch, making me a novelty.

I must have inherited imitation from my mother, though it has manifested as dishonesty. Both are simply variations of presenting an artificial version of yourself. My father found the copybook because I showed it to him, went running to him, giddy, thrilled. Let's laugh at silly Mammy together, I thought. She's written a story, I said. But I got a fright when I saw him grow rigid while reading it. I didn't know then that men could have their feelings hurt as badly as women, as badly as small children. I didn't know how easily hurt could be supplanted with anger.

How is it that she and I are almost the same and yet while she offers me an unfaltering and unconditional love, I cannot forgive the person she is? Even when I know the house she came from. How can I forgive Granny's negligence and my father's strange anger but withhold the same from her? What does it say about her that she tolerates it? My gaze falls to a picture of her and Daddy at the beach. With a burgeoning worry I wonder what it says about me.

II

I am flanked by my mother and daughter at my kitchen table. I can feel a hot pain in my eyes as the sun dips below the end of the garden and I know I should switch on the big light and root around for my glasses. But I cannot tell you how reluctant I am to move from sitting between the two of them chatting and pointing and pausing. I'm afraid to move from the rare and tentative happiness, to come back and find that it has passed me. Even the tender spot beside my ear where there seems to be a pimple blooming beneath a darkening mole doesn't distract or upset my mind as it did this morning. My mouth watered with fright and sickness when I ran my fingers across it, something so small and probably innocuous.

How do people not die earlier? There are so many things that can go awry in our bodies. The intricate systems within us keep on working, until they don't.

As a small child, I would sit beside my mother while she sunbathed on the step in our front garden, her bare legs stretched before her. I was fascinated by the risen map of veins traversing her feet, the blood of them chasing the heat beyond her thin skin. I poked them cautiously, terrified they might rupture, delighted and revolted by how freely they wriggled but how unyielding they were to damage. The rest of her body rarely produced anything but damage. Her stomach grew and rounded and shrank again like a heaving chest without creating a child who lived, apart from me and my brother Michael.

For months, I was left to sit beside Michael as he slept during the day in my parents' small, hot bedroom. My mother gave me a small mirror to hold above his mouth. If the reflection wasn't blurred by the fog of his breath I was to call to her immediately. Then what? Well, he lived anyway. Not that he's ever thanked any of us for it. The frameless mirror left pink ridges on my palm and when the cramp in my wrist became too much I would roll away and lie belly down on the dusty carpet. I used to sign my name over and over on edges of newspaper before scribbling it out for fear someone would find it and my vanity would be exposed.

I'm looking at a photo now of me, my husband and my daughter on Dollymount Strand. I don't know if I knew how happy I actually was then. I was so beset by some vague worry and it seemed to occupy my consciousness more than any other emotion. I've never been able to grasp it by its bony shoulders and identify it. I'll turn with a grim sense that it's trailing behind me to barely catch its silhouette slipping back around the door or the wicked tail of it snaking beneath the bed.

Obviously that's not how I described it to Michael's wife. She's forever finding new things to be interested in and this year I notice that she frequently talks about 'practising self-care' and 'being mindful'. She thinks I'm suffering from delayed grief. Nothing delayed about it, I said. It's prolonged and if it's grief then it was pre-emptive because I carried it from my mother's house to my husband's. All that has changed is that people expect you to talk about not liking yourself now. And if you're going to talk about it, you must surely follow this up with a moment of clarity during which you realise you are perfect and always have been. Wouldn't that be fantastic?

This tall and gentle woman, my brother's wife, she asked me to think of a tree. Did I think the tree worried if other trees didn't like its branches? I gave her the same smile I give to that poor header who hangs around Cleary's Newsagents and barks random abuse at everyone who passes him. I smile because I'm too polite to tell him to leave me alone. Michael's wife nodded slowly, satisfied, maybe assuming she had achieved empathy. She didn't press me any further.

Trees don't question their worth in the world for the same reason I don't sprout leaves out of my backside: it's not in their nature.

I am moved by a picture of my father standing beside us on our wedding day. He was an affable sort of man, slow to lose his temper. Why is it that women only marry men like their father if their father is a demon? I married a man like my mother. My husband's anger was quiet but vast. It was like standing at the edge of a cliff, you were always close to being whipped from the brink of safety.

I loved him though, even during the senseless gulfs of silence between us. And my little girl adored her daddy. When we walked home she might be inconsolable with exhaustion and the sight of his car in the driveway was a relief. Oh, oh, look, there now, I would say, pointing ahead, towards the house in an attempt to soothe her. There's Daddy's car! There, now! On those days, it sounded like I was begging.

I loved hearing them play together. It was a joy that eluded me if I ever went to join in. The breathless, hysterical laughter came to an end because now that I was done with the bits from dinner, couldn't I put her to bed? With that she would tumble from his lap and he would sidle by me. I would know that she was looking at me wishing I had made a start on some other thing in another room to lend her another moment to play alone with him.

There will be no more moments for them now. He was gone before ever having to pretend not to know she was jarred coming home at sixteen, before her obsession with weight loss drove me to tears. He missed her first job, her cleverness, her cruelty and her kindness.

My mother's anger was usually only visible from the corner of my eye. But I remember at twelve becoming aware of the new, unpleasant odour that accompanied the first few months of bleeding. I was uneasy and self-conscious, wanting to know how I should properly conceal it but feeling too ashamed to seek guidance. That kind of conflict seems insignificant now but it was a great source of distress for me at that age.

One evening, I was sat next to my mother on the sofa. My brother was lying on the floor in front of the fire and my father was in his armchair. My mother lowered her head to mine without looking away from the television to tell me I was never to go to school smelling so disgusting again. There was a bath upstairs for a reason; not using it was the height of laziness. In her revulsion, she became angry and I couldn't understand why. Michael looked up to my mother, to me and then my father who stared straight ahead. I sat in the blue light of the television, unable to move from of the shock and the creeping shame.

These eruptions abated when she felt they had served a purpose. Michael and I had grown and married and left and she could relax, good for her. It's a pity that I couldn't but I might yet.

It's ridiculous to feel this hurt at my age, by a woman as old as her. But even sitting here now, I feel redundant and flustered. The cautious contentment slips. The lump beside my ear throbs. I feel like I'm still gripping that mirror, clueless as to what I would do if the fog didn't appear.

III

My granddaughter must think I'm about to die. She never invites me to anything. We meet on the anniversary every year in my daughter's house so I don't know why she rang to ask if I was going. Before she hung up she said that she loved me and I felt very frightened.

We're very fond of each other and we're great pals but I see her give out to her mother and I see myself doing it, years and years ago. My daughter is a meek sort of person. But that unpleasantness really was a very long time ago and I'm upset with her for not forgiving me, for not understanding me.

At my age, I forgive myself. The marriage bar was a terrible thing for us. The worst part about leaving your job after the wedding was waiting for the babies to come and fill you up. I was waiting a long time. The loneliness was relentless. The first four times were like a run and jump to reach the other side of a ditch, only on the fifth one did I manage to clear the thorny void.

When I try to remember my daughter as a small child, it seems we spent so much time in bed together. The both of us lying on our side, her bum against my belly and her rough little heels pressed to my shins. Her father was off working for a farmer in the country during the August that she was three. I had her beside me in the bed and a sibling inside of me, the pair of them separated by nothing more than a cloak of skin. Maybe the comfort and warmth of the sheets drew the little one out because we woke, hot and sticky, to blood staining my thighs and her calves. She screamed because she thought the blood was hers. I sobbed because I knew it was mine and someone else's. Of all the times, that was a shock. I denied her father afterwards, for the winter.

That Halloween, I dressed her as a mummy, her little arms rigid as I bandaged them. Her father went off with her around the houses. I stood at the front door for a while after they went. Tom O'Cuiv next door stood at his own step, the pair of us separated by the garden wall. He was from a place near Dundalk. I liked his nearly northern voice, his widening of vowels and his hushing of sibilants. We had chatted like this plenty of times before tonight. But by now, things had well and truly soured for me. The children from neighbouring houses had passed us, carrying oranges and monkey nuts. Would you come in to me, Tom? And he made his way down his narrow path and up mine. As he brushed past me and over the threshold I turned away from the door jamb I was leaning on and closed us in from the smoky air.

It was a brief opportunity, creating a sense of urgency. The moments beforehand were strange; we stood on opposite sides of the hall. I hadn't thought he would be so nervous. While he was still speaking, I lowered my head and hooked a finger between two buttons on his shirt to draw him in. When I raised my eyes to him, I realised that he hadn't been sure what he wanted to do with me until just then. Rather than thinking of myself as beguiling, I felt foolish for having assumed he was submitting to a long held desire. And why did it hurt that he hadn't shared the same designs I had from the beginning?

It was just the once, which makes me think of us both as ridiculous. I held him close to me as I felt him quiver and shudder to an end, a foolish little act.

There were two months of no blood. In January, I put my hand on my husband's chest and tipped my chin towards him as if he were the one to have withdrawn from me. The whole thing happened with his reluctant pleasure and a determination to get what he wanted from the final moments. It was like watching him touch himself. He squeezed his eyes shut.

Imagine. The two of them will be looking at pictures of me soon. Or maybe not. I drop three or four photos that I had been shuffling, though my hands have not been shaking, and they land face down. I lean to gather them but my daughter places her hand on my arm to stop me and reaches for them, while still speaking to my granddaughter, uninterrupted. They smile at me and then glance at each other. I catch my daughter press her lips together tightly and I wish she would be honest, I wish she would stop concealing her harm, the harm she thinks I've done her and the harm she wishes me, however small and private and unspeakable it may be.

And why should I know any better than what I've done? Am I to ask for some absolution? I doubt she will afford it to me.

The truth and experience of things are as evolutionary as words. They shed and then accrue meaning over and over as they are echoed through time and distilled through the cupped hands waiting to claim them, to derive significance and resonance, even when this is painful or futile.

There's a tether that exists between the three of us and I don't know if it's divine or coincidental. But it has been fused ever tighter by our discord. It has grown thick and twisted and sophisticated, beyond reversal, a knotted weave as impossible to undo as all the things of which it is a consequence.

Derrychara

When nougat was *nugget*
and Renault was Ren*awlt*

and Ajax of Amsterdam
was said the same way

as Ajax, the all-purpose cleaner
or the fearless hero of Troy—

he who led the Greek attacks
and covered all retreats.

When Gerd 'Der Bomber' Müller
hadn't an umlaut to his name

and Madrid was not Real but *real*
and I got stuck on *delicatessen*

while reading Minnie the Minx
because we'd no such thing in Enniskillen,

I could have told you, all the same,
what brand of religion you were

by how you said aloud
the townland name of Derrychara—

with the hard *ch* of church
or aspirated and without.

Derry*ch*ara or *Derraharra*—
that's to say Doire Chara

meaning the oakwood of the weir.
Or, as a friend of mine suggested,

Doire *Chora* meaning pot,
cauldron or swirling pool.

John Kelly

Postcard from Madrid

In Madrid for the weekend I'm free
for a reading by Raúl Zurita from Chile.
All the terraces are full,
tattoos ring everyone's arms,
a great spill of plaits
from the girl toasting bread
at La Libre Bookshop & Café.
I'm reading Edna St. Vincent Millay
the ceiling fan spins in the glass
as the light pours pure
through the afternoon and I wonder
when will I see the rain again?

Keith Payne

Five Moments in Sport

Tadhg Coakley

–1–

I have only one memory of my father kissing me. I was eighteen years old. It happened on the long curved platform of Kent Station, Cork, the night after the All-Ireland Hurling Final of 1979, when my teammates and I had brought the minor cup home.

I can recall almost nothing about the match, but I clearly remember the railway station being packed with giddy people when the train eked itself out of the tunnel and braked to a stop. A pipe and drum band was playing full blast. From the door of the train I saw my father approaching through the crowd. I felt the pull of his arms as I stepped down on the platform. I saw the liquid joy in his eyes. The startling bristle of his stubble on my cheek and the scent of whiskey from his breath are as vivid to me today as if it all happened yesterday.

I'm sure my father kissed me as a child; he was a loving and tactile man. I remember his bedtime stories about last-minute rescues in helicopters, but I can't remember any of those kisses. I'm sure he was proud of me on the day I graduated (eventually) from university, and on the day I got married, and the times I looked after him and my mother when they were elderly. But what I saw and felt that September evening as a young man transcended pride. My father was lifted. He was radiant. Because of me.

In August 1998, my father lived in a nursing home in Mallow. He was eighty and he had become very frail since my mother died the previous summer. My wife and I were on our way to a wedding in Galway and, as we approached Mallow, she asked if I wanted to call in to see him. I said no, we'd keep going, and he died the following night while I was drinking and dancing at the wedding.

When my family and I carried his body to his grave, I held that kiss on the train platform close.

–2–

It is 1971 and I am ten years old. I am watching the Cork hurler Con Roche take a sideline cut on a hot day in a heaving Semple Stadium, in Thurles. I am with my father and the Walshs—family friends—and my older brother Dermot has just played with the Cork minors, winning the Munster Hurling Final.

We are beside the sideline and I have a good view of Roche as he bends down in front of us and places the sliotar on the grass. He stands back and lowers his torso in his approach to the ball, as hurlers do. The hurley is swung hard, at an acute angle, into the sliotar. We are so close that I can hear the sound of the hurley's heel slashing into the earth—a dull, meaty thud. The other sound of the hurley's *bas* striking the ball: a gravid pock. The ball rising towards the Tipperary goal, the pitch of the crowd's anticipation rising too— it's a great cut. The ball falling towards the goal, the sound of the crowd deepening and mounting, expectant.

There's a slight shimmer in the distant net and a different roar detonates itself. A concussive wave booms and rolls through the stadium as though it is a living thing, sentient of what is happening.

I sometimes wonder if I'm seeking the sound of that crowd at every game I attend. If it is the cause of my desperate exultation as I sit in the stand and the match approaches. I'm like an addict craving that very first high.

Experiencing that sideline cut compels me, as a boy, to incessantly hone skills and devote myself to playing. Which, in turn, leads to my presence on that same pitch in Thurles, eight years later, playing for Cork in a Munster Minor Final against Limerick. In the closing moments of that game the ball breaks for me, hopping nicely, about twenty-five yards out, and I meet it perfectly, first-time, and it tears into the top left corner of the goal. When the sound of the crowd strikes me—literally strikes me—I have a sensation of being both inside and outside my body, and the blood in my head churns and casts me into a dizzying trance, and I can't hear what people are saying to me until after we return to the calm of the dressing room.

Two games after that, I have my father's kiss.

– 3 –

I was at the Munster Hurling Final in 2010. A child was sitting beside me with his father. The boy was eight or nine. Not long after the beginning of the match, the father and son changed places and I realised that it was because of me. Something I'd said, or maybe shouted or sworn, the look in my eyes, my rigid body language or the tone of my voice, had frightened the child. I might have been roaring my head off and I didn't even notice.

They didn't return to their seats after half-time—the father must have found a safer place in the stadium for his boy to watch the game—and the empty seats were an admonishment all second half. I felt ashamed.

I'm generally a fairly mild-mannered person. I'm not given to hate or violence. But there is anger inside me. I am angry about Trump and climate change denial and all sorts of issues. I'm also probably angry about aspects of my own life. For the most part, I am well able to keep my anger in check, but sport is one of the few areas in my life where the anger can be pried loose.

The usual macho social stigma that prevents men from expressing their emotions is absent within the catalytic invocation of sport. And these emotions are heightened when you add the cocktail of alcohol and gambling and the mob mentality that men use to amplify their passion during games. I was bringing anger to the game when the father moved his child away, but others bring racism, sectarianism, nationalism, violence, homophobia and sexism—all manner of toxic masculine behaviour.

There is so much to dislike in sport. How my love of Manchester United is also manifested through a hatred of Liverpool and how sport facilitates such nastiness and irrationality. How sport discriminates against women: the Irish women's hockey team brought about a wonderful sense of national pride and togetherness in 2018 by reaching the World Cup Final, but had to pay for some of their own costs in London (something their male counterparts would never have to do). Women's teams like Mourneabbey and Slaughtneil and Milford and Johnstownbridge can bring about a deep sense of community spirit—creating social capital and collective identity, inspiring countless girls who have to face barriers their brothers don't need to worry about—but they get almost no press coverage.

These are the two extremes of sport. The yin and yang. Do I adore one and deplore the other? I do. At the same time—like most men—I watch very little women's sport, but I have no problem occupying myself with the billionaire fiefdoms of The Premier League; the machismo and greed-fuelled franchises of the NFL; and the FIFA men's World Cup, which is saturated by corruption. Does that make me culpable, by association? Perhaps.

In her essay, 'Why I Write', Joan Didion says that she began the writing of her book *Play It As It Lays* with two pictures in her mind. The first was of white or empty space. And anything that happened in the book would happen off the page. The book was a 'white' book to which the reader would have to bring his or her own bad dreams.

I think this is also the way we approach every game we experience, be it as a supporter or a player. We bring our own lives and dreams (bad and good, we won't know how much of each until the final whistle), and we are colouring in the white space with them, before, during, and after the game.

When I'm walking in the crowd up St Joseph's Road to Semple Stadium, or down Jones Road to Croke Park, this is what electrifies me most. I'm looking at all these people around me and I'm thinking about that white empty space. A story will unfurl itself in the stadium we're approaching. I know that. But the real story, all the real stories—mine and those of the forty or eighty thousand people with me—have already happened off the page. And what we see and experience in the game is done through the prism of those stories.

The Limerick people at the All-Ireland Hurling Final of 2018 brought with them the hurt of forty-five years of losing—of not being good enough, and the personal failings of their own lives, and the loss of all the people who had not lived long enough to experience that day. The shattering ecstasy that came out of the win wasn't so much because of what happened on the pitch during the game—it's only a game after all—but what had happened over the previous forty-five years, colouring in the white space.

In a way, both sets of stories merge—what happens during the game and what happened in our lives before it. And both are completed in that merging, like in a sexual mating. And we want this merging—it's why we go to games. We want to pour all the emotions of our lives out onto the white space.

–4–

On the night after my last hurling match, when I was thirty years old, I cried in a pub in Cork and the woman I was about to marry had to console me. I cried because we lost and I knew I'd never win a county championship with my club, that I had let them down again. Maybe I cried because I knew I'd never play on a hurling team again and I'd never have that particular type of safety again.

Because there is a *them* in sport—an opponent or other—there is an *us* and this us is the collective. Being safe in the collective is one of the main comforts of sport: Tom McIntyre, the playwright and Gaelic footballer, called it a 'taking refuge in the collective'.

I joined such collectives or teams as soon as I could—my first would have been around the time I was eleven. My own lack of self-confidence was somehow masked in the teams within which I played. Strangely, I hid there in full view—sometimes, later, in the full view of thousands.

I loved having a ball at my feet, playing football on teams—which I did for many years, to a high level. The rightness of being joined to the ball, that sense of being at home on the pitch never deserted me. I was never afraid on a pitch, or unsure what to do. When I was part of a team, I had a purpose, I was useful, I was valued. I belonged there and I knew I belonged there. I felt safe.

Because I was good at sport, I quickly realised that I could get affirmation from it—the affirmation that insecure people crave. The affirmation I now seek from my writing—writing having become my substitute for sport (and I often conflate the two).

The bond that teammates feel is very hard to describe. It's a kind of love—a false and short-lived love to be sure, but the connection is intense and full of shared purpose in those moments. And when I played sport it wasn't the need to win or compete that drove me on or allowed me to achieve, it was the dread of letting my teammates down—of betraying their trust and losing their esteem. When I played well and received their admiration I didn't feel so bad about myself. If others—coaches, teammates and supporters—believed in me, perhaps I could believe in myself. But loss is utterly integral to sport and the final loss is when you can't play any more.

A couple of years after my final game as a sportsman—when I was in my early fifties—I read Helen McDonald's magnificent evocation of grief and healing: *H is for Hawk*. It contains a sentence that impaled me: 'We carry the lives we've imagined as we carry the lives we have, and sometimes a reckoning comes of all of the lives we have lost.' I knew the moment I read those lines that I had to write—I'd put it off for too long and who knew how much time I had left. At first, I didn't know how I'd manage to write or what about, but I figured it out soon enough. I'd given up sport as a player—or rather it had spat me out—but, before long, I was trying to find it again as a writer.

My father's kiss and Con Roche's sideline cut turned up in my first novel, *The First Sunday in September*, albeit fictionalised and from different perspectives. When the book came out, I was asked by journalists if I wrote it because of unfinished business as a player. I think the answer is yes—I needed to process what sport means to me, what it does to me, and what it has been doing to me since I saw that goal and heard that sound when I was ten. I also needed to validate that moment and all such moments.

Albert Camus said: 'All that I know most surely about morality and obligations, I owe to football', and he was right—I have felt this morality and these obligations. Noam Chomsky described sport as the opiate of the people and he was right—I've lost count of how many times I have found myself watching a meaningless game I couldn't care less about when I could be reading or doing something useful. Sport is admirable and sport is deplorable. It promotes volunteerism and greed. It is an innocent pastime and a pernicious addiction. It is the simplest and the most complicated of activities. It means nothing and it means everything. It is motivated by the best of intentions and the worst. It invokes love and hate. It is the cause of ecstasy and agony. It is fleeting and lasting. It can be a force for good and for evil. These contradictions and the cognitive dissonance they evoke compel me to write about sport.

*

At the first round of the Munster Championship in 2017, when Cork had beaten the All-Ireland champions, Tipperary, I found myself with tears in my eyes. It was only a first-round match, in May, hardly critical. I berated myself and then looked at my friend Martin two seats down and his eyes were wet, too. We're two middle-aged men, toughened by lifetimes. We should know better.

In the moment of those games, the emotions are real and intense. But afterwards, do they hold? And how do such emotions compare to what you feel, say, in relation to your family, your boyfriend, your job, or climate change?

Karl Ove Knausgaard writes about the emotion he heard in a Norwegian football crowd in Oslo, shortly after the massacre of sixty-nine young people by Anders Breivik on Utøya Island in 2011, and the collective grief of a whole people in that sound, in its intensity. But, he says, 'The feelings football arouse are an imitation, that is the feelings are genuine enough, but they are not binding, they are not tied to any reality but one which is artificially constructed for us, twice forty-five minutes.'

I think that Knausgaard is wrong.

This Oslo stadium, this sound, is Joan Didion's white empty book and the fans there are filling in the pages with dark colours, as they weep during the national anthems and cheer as the game is about to begin.

Perhaps there is a thread of steel will in the roar of that crowd too. A determination to ensure that the slaughter on Utøya is not Norway, is not those people. A resolve that Anders Breivik and all the Anders Breiviks will not beat them, nor define their country. The sound urges on the Norwegian team to win, to overcome an *other*. And in that winning, the people at the game are not so much yearning for a victory in a mere football match, but a different, allegorical victory over the other—one that is much more important and meaningful and lasting.

This is the significance of Knausgaard's sound. And I believe that the emotions drawn out in that sound—drawn out by football—are not an imitation, but are binding and tied to reality. Yes, sport is an artificial construct and a banal type of play—but the emotions we bring to it, that it draws from us, are real and they do continue on.

In the moment of that sound and those emotions, sport is packed with meaning; it is vital, intense, joyful, heart-breaking, complex, wonderful and lasting. It is motivated by the best of intentions: love. It is a force for good, not evil. And sometimes (not often, I'll admit, but sometimes) we are not the same people after a game that we were before it. I was not the same after my father's kiss.

Maybe I write about sport because of that kiss. And because of all the other kisses, by all the other fathers and mothers and brothers and sisters and friends and wives and girlfriends and husbands and boyfriends and coaches and teammates and delirious fans. I wrote about such a kiss and built a story around it, and built a book around that story.

I know I can never have that kiss again, so I was compelled to write one. I wanted to give thanks for it and to mourn it. My book was published on the twentieth anniversary of my father's death and I allowed myself to confer some significance on that.

I wrote a story where a man kisses his son, who has captained his county to an All-Ireland championship. The kiss is witnessed by the hurler's birth father, who gave him up for adoption as a baby and realises his loss: that he will never bestow such a kiss to his son. I know this sense of loss. I don't have a daughter or a son and so I will never pass on my father's kiss. In reality, that kiss dies with me. My writing of it is an attempt to pass it on. A pale shadow of the real thing, but in that writing I don't feel so alone, or so lost without him.

Sons At My Feet

Grahame Williams

Warwickshire, Wednesday 7th November 2018

Hi	04:11
Your brother rang me last night	04:19
This morning I'm writing you what I told him	04:20
You know I always tried to be fair	04:20
Give you both the same	04:20
And sure you'd not answer if I rang	04:21
Was looking for the delete button there but I can't find it	04:26
They gave me a hammer for my birthday	04:27
Only for use by grandpa it says on the handle	04:27
There it's on the side by the kettle	04:27
Keith next door is already up and out	04:28
Working at his boat over in the field	04:28
Two old men right beside each other in the middle of nowhere	04:28
Anyway these messages will be waiting when you wake	04:29

I'll see the wee blue ticks when you've
read them so there's no need to reply   04:30

I know you hate when I say wee   04:31

Belfast stain I can't get rid of   04:31

He was upset   04:32

Upset's not right   04:33

In bits more like   04:33

And that anger   04:33

In the beginning your mother and I
wondered would you share one
another's pain   04:34

I mean feelings not just pain   04:35

Thought maybe you were born for
each other not just with each other   04:36

Maybe you'd look after each other
if we weren't able   04:37

Sorry needed some coffee there   04:45

Can see my own life in the air   04:45

Jesus   04:45

That should have said breath   04:45

This thing corrects me when I don't
need correcting   04:46

Blame the tools   04:46

You know his boy isn't right   04:47

Have you at least bothered yourself
with that   04:47

Pulled your thumb from your arse   04:47

I'll take the hammer to that thought	04:48
Bang	04:48
Bang bang bang	04:48
There it's hit on the head	04:48
The boy is the boy but it's awful hard on him	04:49
Your brother I mean	04:49
For once things not going his way	04:49
I asked did he remember that time the three of us went out on Lady Christina	04:49
Stupid question	04:49
Near thirty years ago now	04:49
November	04:50
Too late in the year	04:50
The pair of you rhyming all summer you wanted to go sailing for a week	04:50
Boys' Club and no Mum	04:50
I knew a week on the canal would be far too long	04:50
You'd be bored witless	04:51
I was driving home late the Friday evening. Home wasn't great. Work wasn't great. Coming into Nottingham saw this big massive chimney. Red brick and writing up the side	04:52
Back and forth that way years I'd not noticed it before	04:53
& Sons it said	04:53

Yes to hell with it I thought let's Boys'
Club get away on Lady Christina   04:53

For the weekend just   04:53

Let's see how we get on for a weekend   04:53

Straight in the door I told your mother   04:54

Raised you both from bed and packed
for the three of us. Remember you had
the same sports bags. All the different
zip compartments and luminous
orange edging   04:54

Puma was it   04:54

Those bags were the first perfectly
matching things we bought you   04:54

In the early days all your clothes
were got from charity shops   04:55

No chance of us buying the same
outfits and keeping you equal   04:55

That's why I took the job with the
glassware sales   04:55

The money was so good   04:55

Despite it took me away from you
weeks at a time   04:56

That was the price   04:56

So by then we had plenty of money
but money wasn't enough   04:57

Stopped at the mini-market outside the

marina I got soup and crisps   04:59

While my back was turned him and
you picked out a 24 pack   04:59

Budweiser	04:59
American crap I can't stand	04:59
But two ten year olds lugging a big box of beer from the fridge	04:59
That was a sight	05:00
Put me in mind of a pantomime horse	05:00
This is a present for you Dad	05:00
I'd been trying not to drink	05:00
You know things were pretty bad at home	05:01
Anyway I paid for the beer	05:01
By the time we got to Lady Christina it was well past eleven	05:02
Pitch black	05:02
I'd been thinking we'd set off under the stars the way I used to back home	05:02
Out on Strangford in the summers with your grandfather	05:03
Scudding between the wee islands like we were exploring outer space	05:03
A million miles from Belfast	05:03
That's what I'd wanted for the two of you	05:03
Look boys Orion's Belt	05:03
Boys there's Pegasus	05:03
There's Keith down at his garage	05:04
Looking over at my window	05:04
Gesticulating	05:04

Away on Keith	05:04
Away on	05:04
Are you awake	05:05
Are you	05:05
The ticks just went blue on all those messages	05:05
I can see you've read them	05:05
I can see you're there	05:05
Good	05:06
I'll keep going	05:06
There wasn't enough room in the fridge for all the beer. Your brother lined the cans along the floor. Told me to go sit up top and I got my camping chair and even though it was freezing I went and sat on the roof the way he wanted. Could hear crashing about under my feet. Time was I'd have torn strips off anyone damaged Lady Christina but I hadn't the energy	05:08
Looked up and I couldn't see a single star	05:09
How clear that sky was but no stars	05:09
Maybe that's only in my head	05:10
So damn cold	05:11
I'd packed in a rush and forgot blankets and jumpers	05:11
But like magic he hands me a beer	05:11
You hand me a cup of tea	05:11
There I am beer in my right hand tea in my left	05:11

Sons at my feet	05:11
One of the moments of my life	05:12
Ha	05:12
And my life falling apart	05:12
Of course I'd no idea at the time	05:12
You think I always favoured him	05:14
That's not the way it was	05:14
You were meant to be equal	05:14
Don't worry Dad we'll drive the barge and work the locks	05:15
You need to relax	05:15
That was him	05:15
You need to relax	05:15
Except you need to relax was your mother's words	05:16
Her words in his mouth	05:16
Was her made me realise I'm an angry man	05:16
The two of you watching as I drank	05:17
Gulp of beer gulp of tea turnabout until the lot was gone	05:17
I relaxed alright	05:17
Too late to set sail	05:17
The clatter of cans woke me in the morning. Felt like someone had took a hammer to my head. You untying the moorings. Him trying to work out how to start the engine	05:19
Him wearing that bloody captain's hat	05:19

That hat	05:20
Your mother bought it me for a joke	05:20
Gold anchors and all	05:20
I meant to give you both a turn with it	05:20
But your brother knows how to take an opportunity	05:20
There's nothing wrong with that son	05:21
Anyway I did what I could to let you think you were sailing Lady Christina yourselves. Once we'd navigated the marina that was easy enough	05:22
Dad is this as fast as we can go	05:22
This as fast as we can go	05:22
Some of this I'm writing now I didn't tell him last night	05:23
Some of the detail	05:23
Never mind the stars there wasn't a lot to see in the day. All muddy fields and sky. That's the midlands. A nothing place. I'm still shocked it's where I've stayed	05:24
Not exactly Paris	05:24
Not Belfast either mind	05:24
But we thought it would be safe for you	05:24
Not yet eight o'clock and him saying Dad have a beer. You saying Dad have a cup of tea. Up came a plate of burnt toast. Up he pops with a fresh beer	05:25
The ticks are grey	05:27
Come back	05:27

I'll keep going   05:31

I'd a couple of swigs at the most   05:31

Hair of the dog is all   05:31

The pair of you sat watching but you didn't
seem bored   05:33

The sky moving over us   05:33

Beautiful slow   05:33

The wee message by your picture says
online so I know you're there   05:35

Go on read those last few   05:35

There's nothing to be scared of   05:35

Jesus I felt the cold and if I felt it you two
must have been foundered. If we could
get to a place I'd find a shop and buy us
jumpers   05:36

We reached the first flight   05:36

You pair near dead to show me you
could work the locks   05:36

Stay there Dad stay there we'll open
the locks   05:37

You need to relax   05:37

There was no way you could work them
on your own   05:40

It's a man's job   05:40

Even an old man like me   05:40

You need to know what you're doing   05:40

At both ends of the lock are gates and
paddles. You've to raise the paddles to
empty the lock for going up. Then open
the gates and the barge enters the lock.
Close the gates. Open the paddles at
the opposite end to fill it. Open the gates
and you let the barge leave the lock.
Drop the paddles. Close the gates   05:43

I suppose it's grand if you take it slow   05:44

Still don't know why I left you to it   05:44

There were dead cigarettes floating in the
canal just off the back of Lady Christina   05:47

Pure white with the ends burnt black   05:47

I wouldn't remember them cigarettes if I'd
been drunk   05:47

An empty packet too   05:47

Red Marlboro   05:49

I can feel the weight of the can in my
hand now   05:50

Near enough full   05:50

Blue ticks   05:51

You're with me again   05:52

Jesus the sound   05:53

At first I thought it was a bird flown into
a barbed wire fence or some such   05:54

Made everything seem big around me   05:55

That makes no sense   05:55

Next thing it's shouting for someone   05:56

Shouting for dad   05:56

For a second I'm wondering who's that   05:56

I'd been asleep my whole life and just
woken up   05:56

Do you know what that feels like   05:56

Do you   05:56

You've not the slightest notion   05:56

Sleepwalking through your life   05:56

Wasting all was done for you   05:57

There's another thought for the hammer   05:57

Bang   05:57

I thought you must have fallen in the lock   05:58

Knew it would be you not him   05:58

No splashing though   05:58

Then him   05:58

Dad Dad Dad   05:58

How slow it all went   06:02

Him with his arms around you hunched
over the gate   06:04

Screams coming right out of your bodies   06:04

Put my arms over you   06:04

Felt the scream in your shoulders   06:04

The teeth of the gate   06:04

Your wee fingers caught   06:04

But you know all this   06:05

Then we were through the muck of
the fields   06:07

Toward what I thought was a road   06:07

Falling through hedges   06:07

Muck and blood   06:07

Sliding and sinking   06:07

Christ didn't it turn out to be a motorway   06:09

The roar   06:09

Everything too big too loud   06:09

Coaches and frozen food lorries   06:09

Rush of wind off the lorries   06:09

Two boys and a man caked in muck on the
hard shoulder   06:10

Held you tight to my side   06:10

Him trying to flag a car   06:10

Waving his arms yelling   06:10

Sorry   06:20

Finally that woman pulled over in her van   06:21

All I could say was thank you thank you over
and over   06:21

The three of us jammed in the passenger
seats   06:21

You shivering on my knee   06:21

To begin with I felt lucky it was her found us   06:23

She talked all sunshine like a children's TV
presenter   06:23

Near enough a child herself   06:23

Asked was anyone else hurt   06:24

I said no thank you   06:24

There's only us   06:24

Only us hurt   06:24

Everything I said came out wrong   06:24

And the more I talked the more I felt dirty
Belfast in my voice   06:25

You two with your smooth clean English
not saying a word   06:25

Her with the TV voice   06:26

Van Minister   06:27

That's what he says it said on the front
of her van   06:27

Your brother   06:27

I've no memory of that   06:28

On the side all sayings from the Bible   06:29

Jesus Christ is alive others are dead   06:29

I thought it was just a white van   06:30

Didn't she come with us into the children's
a & e. The nurses took you away off into
a wee side room and him and I waiting
outside with her. All these plastic toys
about the floor and murals on the walls.
A pirate ship   06:33

So you don't know this bit   06:34

She's up at the front desk talking away
to the receptionist   06:35

Shaking her head	06:35
I can't hear what she's saying	06:35
I know she's talking about me	06:35
I'm on my feet saying go on there's no need for you to be here with us	06:36
You've done enough	06:36
You've been too kind thank you please go on your way	06:36
Keep thanking her	06:36
She won't look at me	06:36
Thanking the nurses too	06:37
Everyone in that waiting area	06:37
Saying to the other families aren't they lucky to have such wonderful nurses	06:37
Wonderful women	06:37
Won't look at me	06:37
Thank you	06:37
Thank you	06:37
Won't look	06:37
And she won't leave	06:37
Bitch won't go	06:38
Your brother telling me stop	06:38
Be quiet Dad	06:38
Dad stop	06:38
Imagine that	06:38
Your own son telling you stop	06:38

Imagine	06:38
In front of everyone	06:38
Like I'm the bloody child	06:38
Then the others come in	06:39
Sir please calm down	06:39
Dad	06:39
Sir	06:39
Sir	06:39
Sir have you been drinking	06:39
A man in a shirt and tie and a security man	06:40
Sir what are you doing with these boys	06:40
All sir this and sir that	06:40
Cards round their necks with their faces on	06:40
Told them exactly what I was doing	06:40
Sir how do we know these are your sons	06:40
Sir can you prove these are your sons	06:40
Sir how much have you had to drink	06:41
He's my dad your brother says	06:42
I'm getting him away for the weekend	06:42
He needs to relax	06:42
I'm busy thanking the whole place again	06:43
My voice filling the air	06:43
It doesn't matter what I say no more	06:43

Security man forces me into a chair	06:44
Lays his hand on my shoulder	06:44
Damn near crushes my shoulder	06:44
The woman with her eyes on me	06:45
My fists clenched tight and shaking	06:45
I was on the edge alright	06:45
Then you come out of the wee room with your fingers in bandages	06:46
Eyes straight to me	06:46
Like you're wondering am I okay	06:47
Like you're worried about me	06:47
Jesus all eyes on me	06:48
But yours	06:49
Yours were the eyes got me	06:50
Christ knows what I'd have done	06:50
Blue ticks	06:52
So you're with me	06:52
I've half a mind to ring	06:53
Will you answer	06:54
I'll ring	06:54
No	06:56
I'm not going to give up	06:57
Go on answer	06:59
Answer	07:00
What are you afraid of	07:00

Answer	07:00
Is that it	07:01
Fine	07:01
This isn't exactly what I told him last night	07:03
I went wrong somewhere in the telling	07:03
Said it was him got us out of that mess	07:04
His talk and quick thinking	07:04
But he's not the one	07:04
Said the woman drove us back	07:05
And finally she left	07:05
We walked the canal to Lady Christina	07:05
Back on board I was ready to turn for home	07:06
He was all no no no	07:06
Dad you give up too easy	07:06
We have to keep going	07:06
He put the captain's hat on again	07:20
Sat you up top on the camping chair	07:20
Fingers ruined	07:20
God knows what else	07:20
Told me to work the locks when we got to them	07:20
And I did as I was told	07:20
In a couple of hours we passed the chimney I'd seen in the car	07:21
& Sons	07:21

Like a joke	07:21
A big finger saying up yours to me	07:22
What am I trying to say	07:25
He was after advice last night	07:28
Has it so hard with the boy	07:28
I mean what am I supposed to tell him	07:28
Me	07:28
That's not it though	07:29
I wish that canal had been endless	07:32
And we could have kept going and going	07:32
That's not it either	07:32
Look it's me made you different	07:34
Me made you the weak one	07:34
Jesus I don't mean weak	07:35
You know what I mean	07:35
That day broke you apart	07:35
That was down to me	07:35
What you could have been	07:36
But it's you he should be ringing	07:37
You're the one	07:37
Have you nothing to say	07:40
Nothing	07:42

Tender Publics

Midway or the midpoint of my life
I understood the need to decompress
There was never enough tenderness in texts
Storms rolled through every day for weeks
I drove through some of them

I drove through many strip malls on the way—it felt familiar
The sign said 'window tinting' or 'sunless tanning'
I drove through and forgot immediately
Along the way were many forms of tyranny
The mist rolled up the mountain as I drove

I rolled the window down and rolled it up again
I said, I can't take you a mile down the road
It was because he was he, not because he was poor
She ate her oatmeal like a much older woman
She furrowed her brow but it could no longer be furrowed
Chemicals and plastics make such differences

Closets and cabinets etc. make such differences
Everybody wants to give me a china set
No one in this life wants a china set
Oh just set her up in a house
No you can't even sell it

Oh I found us a red wooden house by a creek
I found us a white house with a vegetable garden already going strong
Oh I found us a kitchen of windows
I know I said I didn't want to go outside ever again
No but I did

Lindsay Turner

Charm for G.

pearl all night
yellow violence in the grass
I don't know how you could fight them

had a thought, lost it
don't take the debt they offer you
stabbed in the neck at the Regal Inn

in the yellow of the air
blisters from the new used shoes
what should be circling is circling

August you neurotic hallucination
at the top of the building, unrelated
that the sunset only be credible, credible

Lindsay Turner

A Truck of Bees Overturns on the Highway

Piers Gelly

We are night we are shaking we are cubes we are a cube of cubes we are sweet applewood shelves and pollen and poison we are shaking we are still we are her tapping our crate with a key she opens us we are an orchard we are day we are grass and trees and dust and almond blossoms we sting her we are less we are almond blossoms and almond blossoms and almond blossoms and the tops of trees the sky we are her alone in an orchard we gather again she nights us we are cubes we are less we are night we are shaking we are still she opens us we are day we are an orchard we are strawberry blossoms we are the space between the road and the ocean we are strawberry blossoms and the space between the strawberry blossoms we are grass and exhaust and salt air we are less we are the vibrations of her voice as she sings a song we are *crossroads seem to come and go* we are *knowing many, loving none, bearing sorrow, having fun* we sting her we are less we are dust we are poison we are strawberry blossoms we are cooling air we are less we are dusk she cubes us we are night

we are shaking we are shaking we are slamming we are falling we are tumbling we are open but not day we are night we are exhaust we are the truck on its side we are cars stopping we are people opening doors we sting we sting we are a young man running between the cars and tearing at his clothes and tearing off his clothes and smacking himself we are cars arriving we are the bright new days of a police siren are days the color of roses and violets we sting we are less we are cars are people stung are less are everything but our cube we are her climbing from the truck are blood on her face are roses violets cars road firemen in sunflower clothes all around her as she tries to cube us we sting we are less we are her shaking her head we are bright day shining in her eyes we sting we are less we are roses and violets we are people stung we are people screaming we are screams we are *ma'am, we have no choice* we are roses and violets we are *I can fix it* we are less we are *ma'am, we can only give you until dawn* we are her voice stopping as if she cannot speak we are roses and violets we sting we sting we are less we are her cubing us as best she can we are cars lined up far along the road we are rose of dawn we are firemen helping her to cube us we sting we are less we are roses and violets we are her singing we are *crossroads seem to come and go* we are dawn we sting we are less we are the arrival of a rose firetruck we are *it's time* we are *you have got to give me another hour* we are roses and violets and *ma'am, please, it's time* we are sunflower firemen preparing a hose we are *don't do it, don't* we are foam we are white are heavy are less are her pushing the firemen back trying to stop the white we are *please stop* are less are foam are *stop* are white heavy are less are singing are *again the morning's come, again he's on the run* are white heavy are less *Yes* white less less she we sing *Yes I know that he won't stay without Melissa* we sing

FEATURED POET

Dean Browne's poetry has appeared in a number of magazines, journals and anthologies, including *Banshee, Poetry* (Chicago), *Southword,* and *The Tangerine.* He won the Cuisle National Poetry Competition while in secondary school in County Tipperary. Dean currently lives in West Cork and is a poetry editor at *The Well Review.*

Rachael's Coat Inside Out

It's floating on a wire hanger now
from the lowest branch in a corner
of the forest. You unhook it,
thumbs worrying stitches for what
you missed last time in the dark
shifty material lining the interior—
the slit left by a torn-away button,
burns, the nervous designs of moths
flickering in and out of the collar.
Your dreams make all kinds of no sense—

locked cabinets with cobwebs across
the wobbly glass knobs. Rachael
adjusts on her nothing shoulders
the winter coat she wore,
the stitching so gone in the pockets
her hands believe they're bottomless.
She could keep a rat in one, the teeth,
the pink loop of tail, brush against us
this close, and who would even know
what she carried there?

Pine Box in the Flea Market

The japanned pine box
with its cold brass handle and clasp
makes an enigma of the room.
Opening it will be intimate, you think—
like the sudden glimpse of a heel
when she nips to the bath
leaving you and the bedposts to interpret
this new hush.

The box is burnished orange brown,
a finish the tint of Chilean Myrtle
or something choked with paprika,
with corners that could cut
like fishhooks. Watch your thumbs.
You want to poke about inside,
to shuck it open with an oyster knife,
spy in over the pine horizon,
and *whisht* you're saying *whisht*—

Inside? Maybe a bunch of shrunken heads;
a rosary of goats' teeth, bone blushing;
a pair of rusty, rubber-handled pliers;
the peekaboo of a tarantula—
you are a horsefly learning immensity
at the brink of a donkey's ear.

You can just picture shouldering it home
past bleeding candles, black veils,
mourners falling into step
and the shops closing on McCurtain Street.
Someone clips a leash on his dog.

This is the clock's insomnia now—
your shoulder killing you all the way back
to a room on a numberless avenue
where blue snow is falling

Five Leaves Left

Nick Drake doubled up the dose
in his parents' home never having fucked once
in his 27 summers. Biographers know—
greasy combs exposing the facts like lice.
Sad thought, stalk torn up like the fruit tree, roots
to a sky flaked pink, summer flush with chirping
mattresses, lovers blowing sugar in each other's ears
I see him a gentleman of strawberries & water
no ice

It is not enough to persist

On our drive to Clare I mistake Corofin for Coffin
your hand is warm on the gearstick
Imagine pulling open your serge
curtains tomorrow   fog
has made a slurred lens of the window
you'd trusted for blackberries & tractors.
Imagine your dead friends gathered in it, hands
around each other's hips for a big group shot
the photographer's thumb covers in the flash

Small Yellow Spider

I want to take you from that corner you like.
Closer, your figure, complicating the air.
Your invitation: to wonder what it's like sightless,
the heart, bloody muscle, humming
through your wires. The blind brush of your leg
my thrill. In the end you may not want me.

Before bed I will forget to close the window.
Here's a good dark spot you can crash in. I'll lie
face up on the floor and the air gets tighter.
We will talk around our wants. It is modest.
I'll feel your hunger grow above me, and will wait
for you to sly down, bite my neck.

A Recipe for Chilli

I'm catching the back garden in a colander held up
to the kitchen window—catching, rather, the fierce green glare
that filters in. When I've had enough I turn, think
If I took a hacksaw and cut up the kitchen table
piece by piece, at what point exactly would it cease

to *be* a table? Which leg if any contains essence of table?
This kills time. Soon you will be home from a late shift
and I'll have cooked us a vicious chilli, spitting
with onion, tomato, the red and yellow peppers, lentils, beans,
dashed with paprika, cumin… too much habanero.

Now they're mingling, ready to have their tantrum
on our tongues. What's left but to uncork a *Côtes du Rhône*
and rearrange the sitting room, in my head? There is no
TV, so all the furniture points to the furniture.
I slug down half then, one by one, tip up the chairs.

Approach to an Egg

A boiled egg is a fresh beginning
and you tap the pale frangible shell
so delicately with the edge
of your spoon, you could be a convict

careful not to wake your cellmate
while you test the walls for weak spots,
brow glazed in response to a sun
rising the other side

Black Cats

Dean Fee

The albino boy was named Calvin but we called him Casper. He had a thumb missing on his left hand that he told us was from a fireworks accident. He was new to our street and came from a whole other county, one away over the road and only known to myself and the others as an outline on the map or a waypoint on our constant recanting of the thirty-two counties. His missing thumb was strange in that it didn't repulse us as much as it intrigued us, so we hooked an arm or two around his neck and dragged him down the back lane to our secret spot.

The verge that ran along the back lane was thick with briars that had gnarled brown and sharp, and yearly produced blackberries that were bitter in the mouth and riddled with pips which we'd spit. The estate dogs had burrowed a tunnel through these brambles, creating a warren-like thicket none of us could enter. We called it the dog tunnel. I had claimed in full voice that my dog had done the doing, that she owned it.

The boys said my dog was dead but she wasn't. My mother gave her away to a farm. She was too wild to be kept in a council house with a garden the size of a stamp. She'd curl herself into knots trying to run around in that thing and once the night came, she'd pine to be let inside to the warmth.

She can pine all she wants, my mother would say. The house is no place for a dog.

But she's cold, mam.

Well, go out and give her your blanket then.

In my blanket at night, that pining panged my heart.

*

Casper's accent wasn't like ours. It was clipped, like he was embarrassed to linger on a word for too long. We liked to dwell on our words, adding an extra syllable or two.

What's the story with your hair? Why's it white?

Do you burn up in the sun?

Yeah, he said.

Like an alien or something.

Yeah, he's like an alien.

Or a ghost.

Is it true a banger blew off your thumb?

You forgot to throw it? You stupid prick.

No, it wasn't like that, he said. I watched it burn down and just as I went to throw it, an older lad, his name was Niall Logue, put his hands over my hand and the banger blew up and blew my thumb off.

Fucking hell. Did it hurt your man too?

Where's the thumb now?

No, but he got expelled from school and his family moved away. We had a big talk after that about safety and they brought me up on stage during school to show my hand. I never found the thumb.

Give us a look again.

He held out his hand palm up and I couldn't help but think it looked like a human fork. The skin where the thumb should have been was shiny and taut and puckered, and he showed us that there was still a little bit of bone left that he could wiggle. It looked like something trapped.

Jesus. What a cunt.

Casper just nodded.

Did your dad kick the shite out of him?

I don't have a dad, he said.

Fireworks were hard to come by unless you had a rebellious uncle or older brother who had a car and could drive up the north. There was a black market up there that sold everything from CDs and DVDs to rip-off soccer jerseys and fireworks. Since my dad was a prick, I had an uncle who looked after me when my mother couldn't. He was a lot younger than my mother and would take me with him when he made the trip to get fireworks. I'd watch from the car as he went around the back of tarpaulin stalls to make shady deals with lads who had stronger accents than our own.

He'd stow the haul in a black plastic bag under the passenger seat and cover it in jackets. My feet could rest lightly on it where it stuck out and it felt like if I applied any pressure the whole lot might go off and we'd be sent flying into the air and maybe even up past the clouds. There was never much fear of being caught crossing the border because my uncle would always do the trip a month or two before Halloween, before the guards started to clamp down on the smuggling.

Once we were home and in the sitting room, he would push the coffee table to the side and lay the bag down on the carpet.

Careful, he'd say. She might go.

I'd bite my lip and squeeze my hands, waiting for the big reveal. He'd reach into the top of the bag and fumble around with his tongue out and his eyes to the ceiling, sending the shits up me sometimes, by banging his free hand on the table and screaming. When he was finished laughing, he'd pull the bag off, producing another wrapping, this time soft cloth often patterned like a tea towel. This he would peel back with pinched fingers to reveal the fireworks.

They were fanned out, tiny sticks bunched together at the bottom that grew to rockets at the top. There were usually about twenty small squealers, papered in stars and moons, and ten big ones, red and black, Roman Candles, and one huge one that looked like the rockets from the cartoons. I could see Wile E. Coyote carting this one off down the desert in search of the Road Runner. There were also Black Cat bangers collected in red boxes. I was given a box and told to not blow my hand off like the albino kid. I promised I'd be careful and was let go. My uncle didn't care much what I did when he was supposed to be minding me.

Cats weren't very well loved where I grew up. It wasn't unusual to see one getting a good boot up the hole for cuddling too close to a standing leg. Or picked up by the tail and swung. My uncle was widely reported to have lined up a litter of kittens at a feeding trough, waited until they were nice and settled, lapping straight-from-the-cow milk, before sighting them down the barrel of his shotgun and firing. He wanted to save bullets. They say the shells made it all the way through to the last cat, claiming up on eighty-one lives all told. He bundled them into an old coal sack, collected the un-lapped milk for re-use, and threw the sack into the lake. I always wondered why he didn't just skip the shotgun and throw them straight into the lake. He told me later that if you died in a room with a cat it would only wait about a minute before eating your eyes out of their sockets.

Mam was walking me to school when I saw the cat blown up in the phone box. It was cold, because around here autumn only lasts about two weeks before turning to winter, and even early morning seemed like a signal to sleep. Mam asked me how the weekend with my father went and said she hoped I had my homework done. I told her I had fun with Dad and my homework was done. Neither was true. I had spent the weekend watching my father drink brandy and listening to him tell me that my mother was a bitch. She, the bitch, noticed the cat before me and uttered an *Oh God* before affecting a brighter tone and asking me if I was looking forward to school. I looked up at her and followed her eyes across the green to the phone box. The glass panels, usually clear, were smudged pink and white. They had stuck a Black Cat banger up the cat's arse.

In class I told the lads what I had seen. They didn't believe me so I suggested coming back at lunchtime to boost each other up to have a look over the wall, but by the time the lunch bell rang and our heads popped over the top there were men in yellow coats hosing down the box with cigarettes hanging out of their mouths. When I passed it on my way home, it was like brand new, like nothing had ever happened.

Halloween was getting closer and the days were barely making an appearance before slinking back into evening. When it turned dark, I met the boys down the back lane. They knew I had my uncle's bangers and were waiting for me. We huddled together, circling the flame of a white Bic, attempting to light a Black Cat or a squealer, sometimes a screamer, and we talked again about the phone-box cat and we all laughed. I said I thought it was hilarious.

Now just fucking peg this once it lights, the banger-holder was told.

The lighter flailed in the wind as we closed in. It was cold and we could feel the meagre heat from the flame.

Get tighter, said the banger-holder.

Casper get in, quick.

Casper had only been in our town about two weeks and found himself on the lowest rung, the butt of the jokes and the one who got told what to do. I was just glad to be elevated a step above him. When he didn't move to close the gap, I digged him in the ribs to get him going. The group nodded at me and Casper edged in but turned his face out to the black stick trees with their whisper and rustle.

Closer.

It started to heat up. Dogs howled in the distance, up the fields.

Pity there aren't any cats around, was said with a laugh.

Whisht. It's gonna catch.

Fuck.

I went to bolt but it hadn't caught, not that time. But then it did. Lines of fire spit from the wick and broke our circle. We clamoured for cover, ripping our hands on the rough cinderblocks that sectioned off the back gardens of the estate's houses. Nobody looked to see where the banger was thrown. We gave in to its random fall, take it or leave it. You might hear it explode with a dull thump in the grassy hill that ran along the length of the back lane, or you might feel it push air against the leg of your trouser and split your ear with a crack.

We were found lucky, half hanging over gates and walls, gazing back to see a sinuous cloud of smoke rising from the bank before being taken by the breeze. The laughter and cheering that followed was riddled with relief. You could see it in the eyes of the others as surely as you knew it was in yours. In the banger-holder, you could see it in his hand and its tremble, and his voice and its warble.

That was fucking mad.

Who's next?

Not me.

Not me, either.

Go on, you pussies. I already did it.

No fucking way, man.

I called for Casper to do it, but the call didn't get picked up by the rest.

Once you've made it through the dog tunnel you'll be one of us, we said.

We were smoking butts of fags stolen from ashtrays and huffing Lynx cans through a jumper up the back lane. The aerosol made you dizzy and sometimes so numb you could throw yourself onto the trodden mud and feel no pain. Things weren't real. Some of the boys said it made bubbles in your brain but that didn't scare me because I didn't believe them. They were always trying to mess with me.

With giddy delight we jostled Casper with our shoulders.

Go on, Casper.

You can do it.

If any of us can, you can.

Casper toed the soft dirt and mumbled something about not wanting to do it, but our cheers drowned him out, and he was pushed towards the bank. He stumbled on with his head hanging and swivelled to look back at us before kneeling down in front of the maw and staring in. He turned again and said he didn't want to do it, but it was too late for that. He was there now.

Go on, Casper.

If you don't go in yourself, we'll make you.

I stepped forward and flicked a match at him. It flared up and shot towards him like a comet, extinguishing as soon as it landed on his alien skin. He cried out and stared back at me, at all of us, before bowing his head and going in. He placed his hands and knees with tender care, pulling back every so often when he got jabbed by a thorn, and we walked the lane alongside him as he crawled, calling his name and howling with laughter every time he got a prick or caught himself on a branch.

Go on, lad.

Yes, Casper.

It must've taken him about ten minutes to do the full length and by the time he emerged, covered in twigs and leaves, his face had been cut and his thumbless hand was bleeding badly from splinters. He climbed to his feet and tried to palm the muck from his knees as we encircled him with our arms and yelled: *One of us! One of us!*

I thought it would have been incredible to be in the middle of that heat, our voices a cacophony in his ears, but as soon as he was released, he wiped his eyes and ran home.

The next day I called for him to come out and play. He answered his door in his slippers and said he didn't want to come out, so I explained that it was just him and me and that I had a trip planned. I was sick of the other lads saying my dog was dead and not out at a farm, so I had asked my mother exactly where the farm was. She said it belonged to an old man out the road who raised chickens and grew vegetables for the markets.

And it's only a couple of miles, I told Casper. We can take the bikes. Are you on for it?

He thought about it for a while before nodding.

Our bikes took us down the hill towards the town and up through the main street where they were already stringing Christmas lights in an arch across the road. We cruised past all the shoppers and waved to those we knew before taking a turn down the country road with its stripe of tufted grass. The buildings grew smaller as we passed until all that was left were low bungalows sending smoke up to the heavens. A farmer walked with his hands clasped behind his back and turned a shoulder to watch us pass, giving us a nod.

His house must be around here somewhere.

It's only been about a mile, said Casper.

How do you know?

Going by the signposts. The last sign for the next town said three miles and this one says two.

That's clever. Right, another bit so.

I kicked the right pedal with my toe, stopped it at its peak, placed my foot back on, shouted come on, and pushed off down the road. It was downhill so I picked up speed with furious rotations of the pedals before lifting off my seat and standing as tall as I could, letting the air plaster my hair to my forehead. I wavered left and right, cackling back at Casper who was still a bit behind as though he was riding with the brakes on.

He caught up once the road levelled out and it was him who stopped first, skidding into the road's verge at another sign.

How many miles we done now? I said, wheeling back around.

I gazed up at the sign that had caught his attention. It was made to look like a teacher's blackboard. It was advertising eggs. Half a dozen for a quid, a dozen for 1.50. On the left, a quarter mile, it said.

That has to be him, I said.

Let's go then, said Casper.

We pushed on again, our heads low and our backs parallel to the road. The hedgerows whizzed by and I glimpsed storm drains and discarded plastic bags and an old washing machine angled upside-down in the ditch, caught like some broad-backed wild thing that hadn't the ability to flip itself upright. A sloping graveyard rose to our right and Casper told me his dad was buried up there. We blessed ourselves and turned our attention back to the road until we came upon a small white van parked up beside a stall made from one of those long foldable tables we had in school. We swung one leg backwards across our seats before dropping off the bikes and letting them roll on to fall, wheels spinning, in the verge.

The man rummaging in the back of the van looked up and showed me his bulbous nose all veined and pocked. He said hello, what do you need?

He lost his dog, said Casper. His mother gave it away to a man.

The man dropped his gaze and smiled. He had a handful of straw in his hand and returned to stuffing it underneath the eggs in the basket.

And you think she gave it to me?

She said she did, I said.

He shook his head. Your mother's having you on, lad.

Casper must have seen my eyes because he patted me low on my back and told me to come on.

We cycled back into town and down to the woods where I used to make bowenarrows. It always took ages to find the right stick. You needed to get one with a bit of give in it. I told Casper all this while we walked our bikes over the rough terrain. There were about three different entrances to the woods and we had taken the main road one where you start at the lake and make your way up into the hills. If you went far enough you left the trees behind and came out at one of the highest points in the town and another one of our secret places. The hill was topped by the ruins of three old buildings we called our base. My dad told me they had belonged to an old wizard who had been kicked out of the town hundreds of years ago and that it was well guarded by the local farmers.

By the time we came to the ruins, we had made a bow each and were now looking for arrows.

I pointed at the ruins and told Casper we had a stash of steel nuts in there.

We can put them on the ends of the arrows so they go far and so they do more damage.

Cool, he said.

Once we found our arrows I brought him across the planks we had laid over the mucky ground outside the houses. The houses were low-walled and roofless. The loose cinderblocks allowed us to climb the walls if we wanted but today we went straight for the old kitchen. There was a three-legged table lying on its side which we were in the process of chopping up for firewood, the last piece of furniture to be burned in the old fireplace we often crowded around, and the kitchenette was thick with dust and old beer and Lynx cans. We hadn't started drinking yet: those cans were from the older boys in town, but the Lynx was ours.

I told Casper that the nuts were in the bottom-right cupboard and watched him hunker down to sort through them. I took one of the Lynx cans, covered it with my sleeve and huffed its remaining high. The world went sparkly.

Pick one out for me too, I said, my lips numb.

He said he would. His face and forehead bore red evidence of his crawl through the dog tunnel and I was sorry, but couldn't bring myself to say it. I asked him how his dad died and he said he didn't know what died meant.

I huffed again. It's when you're not here anymore.

Yeah, but where are you?

You're just not here.

Then where the fuck are you? Another voice.

I turned to see all the other boys squatting on the walls with their bowenarrows resting on their knees. The sky behind them was almost white and the wind had risen.

What are you two losers doing here?

It's alien boy and dogless lad.

One has no thumb and neither has a dad.

Where's your dads, lads?

Don't be mean, I said. Mine's working on a farm in Ballyduff.

Just like your dead dog.

They exchanged looks and laughed and told me to relax, they were only messing. What are you doing here anyway? We didn't agree to show the alien this place.

Yeah, but I thought it'd be okay because he's one of us.

One of us, they all said, and laughed again. He's an alien.

And a dog.

We were actually just looking for him to kill him.

I expected another round of laughter but instead they dropped down from the walls and nocked their arrows and aimed them at us. It was too late to tell Casper to run so I pleaded.

Please don't shoot.

Casper dropped to his knees and threw his hands in the air in submission.

I'm sorry, he said. Let me go and I won't come back.

Don't do it, was said.

He's an alien spy and he needs to die.

Please, I said, and all eyes turned to me, asking why I cared so much, maybe I was a spy too.

No, I'm not.

Then you should do the killing.

He should do the killing.

Raise up your bow or be banished from this base.

I raised my bow and Casper reached his thumbless hand towards me, half to stop me, half to protect himself. I wondered what damage the arrow might do to him: whether it would be as explosive as a banger, a complete destruction of his face, or would it be merely a dint in the cheek or a skewering of the eye socket. The sun was pale but the clouds were delicate, so the light was obscured and muddy by the time it reached us, hazing a little through my lashes and creeping through Casper's fine hair to show me his scalp. He was all white and pink and looked like he might shimmer and disappear at any moment and I thought for a second he might not be real. Maybe he was never there. Maybe none of them were, and I was all alone.

To Lough Tay

Can I come in asks
the cat at the door at this
or that but always the same
one door regardless where
on this earth we have
dragged her behind us.

Lough Tay old Wicklow
puddle can I come in
again enter your waters
where a cat might fish
by trailing a hand in
these these and these

small elsewheres
the mill-pond over
the hill the mackerel's
back of a loch seen
from the car, cold waters
breaking against what

far foreign shore.
A goat scales your sheer
basin Lough Tay and
falling the scree rebounds
over the waves to rattle
around the skull

of whoever is there
and my skull too.
Slow but at last delayed
echoes of blank-eyed
Wicklow goats on
the move reach me

and the skin of that
thin umbrella memory
blowing off lands
again in the over-
flown well of your
crinkled blaze of light.

David Wheatley

Fragment #1

leaf
in that spindle
cruse tight
flex upon the luminous
we right each curve
on the turned
earthly
forbidden
sky lining
our hands
clay to soil
brokered
returned
to the pleasure
pulse
of missed paints
those dots
along the pathways
intercepting the experience

Jimmy Cummins

Parasol

A.E. Kulze

She's only known Eli for a week, known meaning *looked upon*. The previous months were a different kind of knowing, known meaning *felt*. In both cases meaning *feared*.

Eli is sleeping on her breast. With Eli she has approached the boundary of life. He has shown her what her body is, which is: not hers. She looks at Eli's head, his downy crown, stuck there. Eli has remade her.

She would like to speak to someone. She calls John at work. She stands carefully so as not to wake Eli, slowly because she is sore. She dials.

John cannot speak. John is busy fixing bodies. This is what John does. He fixes bodies so people can return to them. She will never return to hers again. Or she will, but it will not be the one she remembers.

She eats an apple. Some cheese. She bites the shape of her mouth into each. She is hungry. Soon she will have to slice everything small. She will have to dice. Soon everything will be dangerous.

There was a time, before Eli, when danger was what she went for. Danger was a much older man. Danger was dreaming. Danger was substance and height, defying weakness. Danger was leaving home. Danger was coming back and marrying a nice doctor. Danger is why Eli is here. Now, Eli *is* danger, and danger is no longer fun.

In Eli's room she sits in the giant rocking chair her mother-in-law gave her as a gift. It was her mother's and hers before that. A sturdy walnut with turned spindles, a slatted back. She is a link in a chain, but it will end with her. She has already decided that she will not give the chair to Eli.

She rocks. She wishes she could work.

Eli's room used to be her room. It held her desk and her books. It was where everything happened. It was her life, and now that the room is no longer hers she fears that it may have ended. She told John this, which was a mistake. John said, ridiculous. John said, *this* is your life. But if this is her life then doesn't that mean that what came before has come to an end?

Of course, she loves Eli. But here is the thing about loving Eli: it's like dying. She can only go one way.

Her phone rings. She rushes to it. She would like to speak to whomever it is, to say, hi, please tell me about your life. Tell me what you are doing at this very moment. Tell me about your shoes.

The call is automated. 'Congratulations,' a voice says. 'You've been selected as the winner of a five-day vacation to Orlando, all expenses paid! To redeem this once-in-a-lifetime trip, please press one.'

She does not press one. She would never willingly go to Orlando.

Perhaps this is an omen. Perhaps she is being warned that she will be the kind of mother who takes her child to Orlando, who buys him plastic novelty cups with brightly colored straws. She can't bear it. She hangs up. She looks outside. It is green with the absence of people. There is a wide field, replete with pollinators, and a thick wall of pine and cedar surrounding them on all sides. They poured all their savings into this wild plot of land, a place for him to rest and her to write, but she's begun to resent the solitude. She will take down the NO TRESPASSING signs John has nailed to trees along the property line. She will welcome any forager or hunter that chooses to pass by. She will point them towards the turnip greens John planted for the deer and the places she's seen armadillos. She will let them hold Eli if they ask to.

Eli, touched by some invisible fire, begins wailing in the same wordless way he did the moment he emerged. The sound seemed to scratch at a tender part of her. She thought maybe it was the same part that was damaged whenever she saw horses die in movies. But with the horses she could close her eyes against the horror, remind herself it wasn't real. Now she has to deal with it. She has to bounce and pat and sing, and afterwards she is too shaken to feel relief.

She senses a coolness between her legs. Bleeding again. The bleeding with a pretty name. What was it? Lochia, meaning *blood* and *mucus*. Lochia, which should mean *magic*. She puts Eli down in his crib to clean herself up, setting him off again. She wipes and wipes, wasting toilet paper. She changes her underwear.

She returns to Eli but decides to let him wail. She wants to see how long he will go without consolation, hoping he will exhaust himself. She has never heard of death by wailing.

She is surprised when the wailing becomes a kind of silence. After a while she can't hear it any longer. It has deafened her, defeated its purpose. It is almost as if she is alone.

But this does not last. One break in tone, a coughing cry, and she launches toward Eli, gives her body back. She holds him to her chest. It is enough to kill her, this joy. How she suffers at the hands of it! How wretched, this place beyond love.

Outside Eli's window an older woman wanders across the front lawn, wearing rain boots and an oilcloth coat, silver hair streaming through the back of a baseball cap. She's carrying a plastic grocery bag, empty apart from air. The bag bloats and sags, bloats and sags, as she swings it.

The woman is a miracle.

She takes Eli and walks out to the porch. The woman waves, walks towards her. She removes her cap, wipes her brow, then replaces it. She introduces herself as Jean from down the way. She is looking for lion's mane mushrooms. She intends to poach them in saffron and butter.

'Lion's mane,' Jean explains, 'tastes like lobster.'

She gives Jean access to wherever she would like to go. She tells her to ignore the signs. She invites her inside.

'I was thrilled when you guys bought this place,' Jean says. 'It just sat here for so long.'

'I imagine that's why it was so cheap,' she says. She offers Jean the couch in the living room and takes a chair across from her. Jean hasn't acknowledged Eli at all.

'I feel bad for anything that can't serve its purpose,' Jean says.

'Well there were squirrels,' she says. 'We had to bring in professionals.'

Jean removes her hat and coat and places them beside her. 'You should have called me.'

It grows quiet. She fears she has forgotten how to socialise. And she used to have such skill! She could put anyone at ease. She was the person other people looked for at parties.

'So do you have any children?' she says, immediately regretting it. What has become of her? Why couldn't she ask, 'What do you do?'

'No,' Jean says. 'I'm not married either, if that's where you're going next.'

'Oh,' she says.

'No divorces,' Jean says. 'Just disdainful towards the institution.'

They grow quiet again. She'll let Jean speak first. Jean is beautiful, she decides. Jean's eyes are violet. She wishes she could look like Jean.

'Do you have any children?' Jean asks.

She doesn't understand the question, places her hand on Eli's back. 'Just this one.'

'Oh dear god,' Jean says. 'I'm sorry. My vision. I don't know what I thought that was.'

Eli makes a brief, wet noise with his mouth as if he knows he's being acknowledged.

'Can I see its face?' Jean asks.

She turns Eli around, holds him out for Jean to see.

Jean leans forward, narrowing her eyes. 'Fascinating.'

She looks at Eli's face too. She wonders what is fascinating.

'I can't see you,' Jean says.

'What do you mean?'

'I don't see you in its face.'

'Oh,' she says, drawing him against her shoulder, her hands cupping the gentle curvature of his bottom and head. 'Well, he's mine.'

'I don't doubt it,' Jean says.

'Can I get you anything?' she says. 'Something to eat or drink?' She would like to have a cocktail with Jean, something to resuscitate her charm, but there is nothing in the house.

'Water, please,' Jean says. 'And something green?'

She brings Jean a glass of ice water and an apple. Jean polishes the apple with her blouse, then bites from it in a loud and satisfying way.

She watches Jean eat, her strong jaw chomping on the flesh. Eli grows vocal, a little restless. He needs to eat too. 'Do you mind if I nurse?' she says.

'Go ahead,' Jean says.

She slips one arm out of a sleeve and pulls the T-shirt up over her shoulder. She helps Eli find her breast. She wonders how much she can tell this woman.

'It's a boy?' Jean says.

'Yes.'

'What's his name?'

'Eli.'

'Eli,' Jean says. 'Is that religious?'

'I don't know,' she says. 'We just liked the name.'

Jean eats the entire core, seeds and all, then picks the flesh from her teeth with her pinky nail. 'So why did you want children?'

'It was unplanned,' she says, covering Eli's head with her hand. 'Not that we regret it. We don't regret it at all. Why didn't you want children?'

'I'm no expert in gentleness,' Jean says.

'I'm not either,' she says. From as far back as she can remember she was better at ruining things; she popped the heads off dolls, broke bones, scuffed up her shoes. She couldn't fry an egg without the yolk rupturing. 'I think my nature is inclined towards violence.'

'Well, of course,' Jean says. 'That's why they expect us to be gentle.'

Jean rises, says she better get going. She puts on her hat and coat.

'Come back tomorrow?'

'I'll bring you some lion's mane,' Jeans says. 'It lifts the mood.'

She wakes up to John wiping her hair from her face, her mouth hanging open, moist at the corners, Eli tucked between her arm and her side. John is standing over the couch, over her and Eli, holding his phone. 'Pretend you're sleeping again,' he says. 'I was about to take a picture.'

'Please don't,' she says. She pushes the device away.

'Jeez,' he says. 'Fine. How was today?'

'Better than yesterday.' She wonders whether or not she should tell John about Jean, if it would anger or worry him that she had invited a stranger inside.

'That's good,' John says. 'I told you you'd feel better eventually. It's normal for the first few days to be tough.'

'I wasn't aware you'd given birth,' she says.

He puts his face close to Eli's, speaks to him as if he were a puppy. 'I went to medical school,' he says.

She used to love everything about him. His plain charm and careful grooming. His belief that he'd rescued her from something. Even his rehearsed, sober bedside manner, which she got a glimpse of whenever she was sick.

'I wish I could stay home,' he says.

She curls onto her side. 'No, you don't.'

'What do you mean?'

'If you knew what it was like, you wouldn't wish for it.'

'Well, what's it like?'

'Colonialism.'

He lifts Eli into his arms, ogles him with the ridiculous smile reserved for the small and helpless. 'I don't know what your mother is talking about.'

'I didn't expect you to,' she says, rising. 'I'm going to take a shower.'

'Take your time,' he says.

He is always granting her permission.

Jean returns around noon the next day with her hair in braids and a small dish of lion's mane. It does taste like lobster.

'I'm glad you like it,' Jean says. They're seated across from one another at the kitchen table, Eli between them, lying on a little round pallet, his blanket patterned with woodland creatures. 'I don't have patience for people who can't appreciate delicate flavours.'

'Well I appreciate them,' she says. 'There really isn't a food I don't like. John, on the other hand, won't eat cilantro or shallots or olives. And he'll only eat tomatoes when cooked.'

'How childlike,' Jean says.

She wonders whether or not to defend John. There are things about him she still finds redeeming—his love for her, for example—but she also doesn't care whether Jean likes him or not. He is not a part of this.

'Then again,' Jean adds, 'most men bore me. Even their lovemaking bores me.'

Lately, she's felt the same way. Ever since she became pregnant John has treated her very delicately. At first she found it sweet. Then it began to bother her, how conscious he was of her changing physiognomy, his careful, lustless handling. He made her feel like a girl.

'What about women?' she asks.

'We're only boring when we're too young,' Jean says. 'Before we realise what we have.'

'I remember being that way,' she says. She looks at Eli, wonders how fluidly he will inhabit his desire.

'Young men can be that way too, you know. I'm training one now.'

'Training?'

Jean removes the rubber band from the end of one pigtail and begins unwinding it, then braiding it again. 'I started seeing a younger man, and I'm teaching him how to please me. He's become quite good.'

She secures the braid with the rubber band, places her hand on Eli. 'I hope you're listening, little bean.'

She wants to show Jean his nails, which move her deeply, a reminder of how exquisite he is, this life she made. But she resists. 'Can we do something?' she says.

'Would you like to go mushroom hunting?' Jean says.

'Sure,' she says, thrilled to be invited somewhere. 'But I need to change.'

'Go on,' Jean says. 'We won't move an inch.'

In the bedroom she puts on maternity jeans and John's painting shirt, a torn flannel streaked with the same eggshell white as their walls. When she returns to the kitchen, Jean has emptied the fruit bowl and arranged the fruit around Eli, a banana neatly aligned with the arc of his head. 'It's a still life,' she says. 'The Fruits of Labour.'

Eli seems unfazed, appropriately inanimate, but eventually begins to wail.

'It's ruined,' Jean says. 'He only needs you because you're here.'

She knows, can feel Eli's yearning like a cramp. She wraps him in a sarong.

Jean leads them into the woods, into a part of her property she's never seen before, a dense stand of pine, the ground blanketed in copper needles and cones. It smells like rosemary. She is happy to be out of the house. Away from its bleached walls and folded linens, from its scent: a sour intermingling of human hygiene and love.

She follows Jean, who pauses occasionally to sniff the air, braids hanging evenly over her breasts.

'Ah!' Jean says, stopping suddenly. 'Come here.'

She walks over, stands beside Jean.

'This,' Jean says, pointing to a white mushroom with a wide cap, 'is a false parasol. It's highly poisonous, but people are always mistaking it for its edible cousin.'

'Okay,' she says, staring down at the little demon. It's pale and fleshy as Eli's fist, but flecked with a few brownish scales. She kicks it, revealing its gilled underside.

'Take a good look at it, so you remember,' Jean says. 'Everyone should know these things.'

They walk so long that Eli grows hungry. She unbuttons her shirt beneath the sarong, guides Eli to her nipple. She likes following Jean. She would like to follow Jean forever.

They pass a swampy area, where shallow pools stand laden with mosquito larva, then encounter a sprawling live oak whose branches bend lazily toward the ground. Near its base Jean locates a patch of chanterelles, absurd in colour, shocking in a terrain of brown and green. 'My,' Jean says. 'Look at those beautiful babies. What a wonderful orange!'

Jean demonstrates how to cut the mushrooms at their base with a buck knife and then hands the blade to her. 'Go easy,' Jean says. 'They won't resist.'

She severs the entire patch. 'How are we going to carry them?' she says.

'I'll take that,' Jean says, gesturing at Eli, 'and you can fill the sarong.'

Eli, full of milk, has fallen asleep. She unlashes him from her body, places him in Jean's arms. She fills the sarong with mushrooms. They walk. Her load is weightless. Her limbs are reeds. Jean's knife is cool in her pocket.

Jean is holding Eli like a forklift, her forearms rigid and parallel to the ground. She careens through thickets, kicking up leaf and muck along the way. Eli wakes up without crying, stunned into silence by the ride. She is in awe of Jean, of Eli, orphaned in her arms.

But then she hears Eli coo, and she wants him back. 'I can carry him now,' she says. 'If you would take the mushrooms.' But Jeans insists. She will carry Eli all the way home.

At the house, Jean asks to hold Eli a little longer. She requests the rocking chair from Eli's room. 'I'm testing a theory,' Jean says. 'It's been widely discredited, but you never know.'

She wipes the mushrooms down with a moist paper towel while Jean rocks with Eli in her arms. She is surprised by how carefully she can handle the mushrooms, patting at their naked flesh, softly blowing them dry in the bed of her palms. She places all the mushrooms in a wooden salad bowl and sits next to Jean. Eli is grasping the end of one of Jean's pigtails. It has been an hour since he has cried.

'You won't believe what I heard on the news yesterday,' Jean says. She is holding Eli against her breast. She gazes down at him, offering him the full expression of her face. 'In Nigeria, female suicide bombers have begun carrying their infants to avoid detection and then sacrificing them along with themselves.'

'That's the worst thing I've ever heard,' she says. She does not understand why Jean is telling her this, what she could mean by it.

'Yes,' Jean says. 'But don't you think there's something pragmatic about it? Rather than abandon their babies, they just take them along.'

Jean is rocking wildly, gathering momentum. She is sure the chair will break.

'What would you do?' Jean says.

She looks at Eli's fist again, Jean's hair between his fingers, and wishes he would let go. She doesn't know what she would do. She needs time to consider what's best for Eli. 'I'm a good mother,' she says.

'You don't think those women were good mothers?'

'That's not what I'm saying,' she says. 'Can I have my baby back?'

'You wouldn't want to wake him up would you?' Jean says. 'Why don't you take a nap?'

'I'm not tired,' she says.

'Don't lie to me,' Jean says. 'You look exhausted.'

'But he needs me.'

'Not at this very moment.'

This is true. Eli is sleeping sweetly in the cradle of Jean's arms, his fist still tight around her pigtail.

'Just relax,' Jean says. 'We'll be right here.'

She tries to remain vigilant, but Jean was right. She is exhausted. And the couch is so soft, and if she just lies down, she could close her eyes gently for a moment and breathe.

She wakes to John sitting on the edge of the couch, removing his shoes. It's dark. The moon is hidden. She sits up. 'Where's Eli?' she shouts.

He hushes her. 'Asleep,' he says. 'Right here. Everything's okay.' He kisses her cheek. 'I'm glad you two are getting plenty of rest.'

Eli is on his pallet on the floor beside her. He is on his back, his fists unfurled in sleep. She moves to the floor, lies down, rests her hand on Eli's chest. The bowl of his ribs fills and empties, fills again. She curls herself around him, a creature and its shell. 'It's not safe here,' she says.

Notes for a Film

for Benjamin Alire Sáenz & Angela Kocherga

Scene I
EXT. Texas borderlands – midday

The picture in my mind is more
than I'll ever be—

the hands, the wall, the kids
desert mountains make

blankets of sky
and thousands of miles away

across too many seas to name
history slouches back against

all this forgotten time.

How do you turn movement
into monuments?

The pictures on your screen are more
than you'll ever see—

the crowd, the face, the land
the terrible truth

you can just about say.

What songs do these winds
carry, and how far

before they scatter out over
brown and white and grey?

I have no doubt that seeing
is believing, yet saying what

it is we see is something
different.

The poet tells us we've
misnamed this place.

What if after all
we've misplaced the names?

The painter says the colours are only
ever approximate—

there is no perfect form
for representation.

Even from outside
you might then be led to wonder

how the brown dead earth
gives life to such

immaculate green.

Scene II
INT. Dublin public house – late afternoon

Or is it night now over the river's
divide? Take your time here

before you wander—

the other voice, the one you're born with,
sits well in silence,

despite your living on its
confidence and confusion.

Not far from here and not
long ago (things considered)

an accent cut close to the grave

some say all that's over
and some that it's only sleeping

there is one thing I know that
we ought to tell the truth about:

the image on the wall is of a woman
who will never stay silent,

even though you cannot know her name.

Jonathan C. Creasy

Death Knock

Chris Kohler

They get called death knocks, and it's always the youngest reporter that gets them. Peter didn't recognise the address at first, but as he turned from the old high school, through the winds of the estate and into the driveway, it came back to him. The best of them had chased a boy around the playground and crowded in to watch his only friend pin him to the wall by the neck. After a minute or two the boy had made a noise that sounded like a quack.

Then, for years, in the school and round the houses, they would shout, 'We're hunting! We're hunting!' The boy, and whoever else fell into sight, knew to run before the best of them warmed up and began to enjoy themselves. The crowd would chase and one might peel off wide and herd the boy into a corner where he was pinned and strangled until he quacked or croaked or squeaked, they didn't mind. They called him Duck, it suited him, and he seemed to like it, he always laughed.

On a death knock Peter had to look up the victim's parents and chap their door. If he didn't get them he had to try the aunts and uncles. The parents were always confused, but the wider family would shout, then threaten. By the time he went to siblings and cousins, the word would have gotten round and they would be waiting by the window. Sometimes that was easier, he would raise his hand to say hello and take a telling off, a warning, a chase up the street. Off he would go to the friends, then the co-workers, the teachers, the bosses, until someone would let him know that they were a good person, full of life, cut down in their prime.

Peter took off his tie and threw it on the dashboard. He left his notebook, but set his phone to record when he clicked it. Had he been one of the best of them? Not really. But he had tagged along. A fence ran right along the front gardens of that street. When they had just started at the high school, which was sunken into a divot at the end of the street, Duck had been chased by nearly the whole school. The best of them, and the hangers on too, anyone that liked a loud noise or a fast movement. Everyone seemed to know what was happening, but Duck had ignored them. As he started to walk, then run through the crowd leaving school, dozens of legs went out to trip him, and he danced through them. Legs were pulled back in for the boys pursuing. Duck ran into his garden and latched the gate. Kids laid siege to the fence, pouring over like a horde of enraged barbarians.

Duck's younger sister, now in her twenties, answered the door. She stared at him through two long curtains of straightened hair. Peter lifted his press card and began announcing himself. *Knew your brother, lost touch with him, saddened to hear.* She stepped to the side just as she had for the paramedics and the police, and then the mourners. She pointed along the corridor to the kitchen table.

'I'll go get Mum,' she said, and disappeared upstairs, into shadows tinted purple by the closed curtains.

Peter pulled out a chair and looked around at the kettle, the toaster, the fruit bowl and the stack of junk mail. The hunt had followed Duck into this house. The boys from primary had chased him into this kitchen, underneath the table where Peter now sat. But one of the boys from the year above, who already looked like a grown man, grabbed Duck's legs and pulled him out, dragged him over the lino, round the corner and into the living room, Duck walked backwards on his hands the whole way. Then someone swept his hands away and he cracked his chin off the floor.

Peter remembered it in images that made it unclear where he had really been. Looking through a window or right inside amongst it? He wasn't sure.

There was a pause then. No one knew what to do next. He got a few kicks, but Duck was lucky because before it warmed up his Mum came back from her work. Her car keys in hand, and a bag of shopping she dropped, she started screaming and pushing kids at random, then she noticed her son, and she powered her way through to him, past the crowd of boys running to either side of her and out the door she had left open.

She came downstairs in her dressing gown now, her face pale, her eyes twisted, her lips pursed. Peter let her know who he was, but she knew already. She took a seat opposite him and agreed to give a statement. Quietly, Duck's sister entered and leaned against the counter behind her Mum.

'Can I get you a tea, Mum?' she asked, and set to make one while Peter asked his questions.

Duck's Mum answered them calmly. She gave him the quote he needed, she said that Ducky was a kind boy who had tried to protect others. She said that people were cruel, that they didn't care, the world was like that, you forgot and then you had to remember.

As the kids on the hunt had fled through the house, they turned on the taps, they opened the fridge, they stole fruit. One took a handful of cutlery and threw it in the garden, another broke a mug. A few boys were slapping the windows from outside as everyone ran out. Then they pulled the washing off the line and it was trampled into the grass.

'And if I could get a photograph of you?' Peter asked as he stood from the table.

'What for?' Her hand jumped up to her cheek, blotched and red, then her eyes flitted down to her jumper and joggers. 'I can't really. Not like this I can't.'

'It's not a problem.' Peter held his hand out and touched her elbow to calm her.

She laughed. 'I'm sorry,' she said.

The sister, whose name Peter must have known at some point, showed him to the door and he thanked her.

'No,' she replied. 'I think it was good for her.'

Back in the car Peter checked through his phone in a tangled line that started with old school friends and led eventually to Duck's page, now a memorial, then to her name, Lindsay, and a few pictures of her with her pals, on holiday and at home. He added her, then reversed out the drive.

Dozens of kids had been sat up on the fence, watching through the windows as Duck's house was raided. A few fell backwards, tumbling over each other as everyone raced out the door and leapt the fence or battered through the gate. With all that weight pushing on either side, the fence bowed, then began to creak, then fell and dragged down one, then two, then three houses along, the whole fence, six feet of it split away from the gate posts, then uprooted and tore out the rest. Everyone laughed and cheered. Men from the houses ran out and screamed, flexed their arms and grabbed at random boys, dragging them by the backpack away from the house. They laughed, they threw things, they ran home, splitting up into smaller and smaller groups.

Going Clear: Sense and Spectacle at the Dublin Horse Show
Ian Maleney

Impenetrable silence falls over the crowd, leaving only the sound of hooves on the turf. Watchful eyes follow the Irish rider and his horse around the course. It's a strange feeling—a clustering of attention, a collective holding of breath; everyone waiting to see if the person at the centre of the hush will make a mistake. The rider is determined, focused. He's pushing his horse faster, higher. Down through the centre of the course, turning, resetting, through the water and over the tricky triple combination. On the home stretch there's a wobble as a hoof clips a pole, but nothing falls. Rider and horse straighten up and sprint to the finish. The stands erupt into overwhelming cheers. The commentator's voice booms out across the arena: 'What pressure!'

The Nations Cup is the main event of the week at the Dublin Horse Show. Teams of four riders from eight countries compete in what the marketing spiel describes as 'equestrian sport's oldest and most prestigious team challenge.' These are the very best show-jumpers in the world, riders and horses at the top of their game. It's a multi-stage event, taking place over twelve legs on three different continents. On the line in Dublin: the Aga Khan trophy and a place in the final, taking place in Barcelona in a few weeks' time. On the Spanish coast, a purse of 1.25 million euro awaits the winning team.

Trying to find shelter from the gathering rain, I join a dozen other people huddled at the top of some concrete steps, a small covered landing between the entrance to the bar and the side door of an exclusive restaurant—the Wylie Suite. Packs of former rugby-school boys emerge periodically from the bar. Holding plastic cups of lager in one hand, they raise the flanks of their Barbour jackets against the rain as they make their way back down the steps. To my right, I can see the poshos dining on the balcony of the restaurant, which is sealed now with plastic wrapping to keep out the rain. Though the landing is cramped and awkward, it is actually not a bad vantage point for watching the horses, or for watching people watch the horses, so I decide to stick it out. The stands are full anyway—the notices went up around the grounds yesterday to say that tickets were completely sold out.

After the teams plod around in the rain for a bit, the course is cleared of pageantry and the riders circle back to the pocket, awaiting their call. The objective is to clear every fence in the arena, in a certain order, without knocking any poles, and without the horse refusing to jump. Each rider is timed, and there are faults for taking too long. The team with the lowest number of faults—and, if a tie-break is necessary, the quickest aggregate time—wins the day. The first two Irish riders go clear: no jumping faults, and decent times. The second rider fist-pumps to the cheering crowd as he gallops back to the pocket.

'Which barbecue were you at?' a woman behind me asks of a man in a blue suit. She's just come out from the restaurant to smoke. She's got sunglasses on, despite the rain, and she seems to be on a first-name basis with the British riders. 'Oh, you missed the big one,' she says. 'We had three hundred in the garden Friday night.'

The third Irish rider emerges from the pocket and quietness falls over the crowd again. Halfway through the ride, a strangled, pained sound wells up from the crowd when the horse clips a fence and intensifies as the pole hits the ground. There is a tangible disappointment in the air, which deflates the whole arena for the rest of the round. Anything less than perfection is somehow underwhelming. Just below me, a young girl is audibly frustrated with the rider's fault. 'It isn't easy,' her father says. 'Life isn't easy.'

An elderly man dressed head-to-toe in tweed is trying to gain entrance to the restaurant. He's agitated as he remonstrates with the security guard: he needs to get coffee for the Chinese Ambassador. The security guard is unmoved: the man needs a ticket. Rebuffed, he gives up and heads for the bar instead. A large, sweating man—a vet, according to the lanyard he's wearing around his neck—bursts out the door of the restaurant and blunders into the crowd at the top of the steps. 'Jesus!' he says, though it's not clear where his frustration and surprise are directed. He mops his brow and his eyes dart from side to side as he plots a path forward. The woman in sunglasses has not stopped talking and it is impossible not to hear her. 'Stop running from it,' she says to the man in the blue suit, who is not saying much. She is chastising a mutual friend. 'He needs to confront his finances. He has enough assets, we can turn it around. He's taken his foot off the pedal completely.'

In the second round, a British horse and an Irish horse are each eliminated after refusing to jump. Once again, this leaves all the pressure on the final Irish rider—one fault and it's game over. The rider trots in circles around the vacant pool of grass by the gate, steadying himself for a moment before driving the horse out onto the course. Every eye in the arena is on him, leaning forward in his saddle, guiding the horse around as quickly as he dares. The sound of a single pole hitting the ground is enough to signal that it won't be Ireland's day, and it is Mexico, the surprise package, who claim the Aga Khan Trophy— their first. The cheering is loud and sincere as the team in red blazers parade around the ring. The woman in sunglasses returns for another cigarette. 'Mexico! Tequila!' she shouts. '*Olé Olé Olé!*'

*

During the first 'Leaping Competition' at the Dublin Horse Show, which took place on the lawn outside Leinster House in 1868, there was just a single obstacle: a stone wall, five foot six inches tall, 'jumped in cold blood off wet sawdust', as one member of the contemporary press described it. The 'Leaping Competition' had no rules as such—the winner was the horse who, in the eyes of the judges, jumped the wall in the best way. This was a purely subjective decision and could lead to disagreements between judges, or between judges and riders. Even if there were no disagreements, the judgements were opaque: a winner was declared, no reason was given. For over half a century, until the emergence of the right honourable W.E. Wylie, this was simply how things were done.

William Evelyn Wylie was born in Dublin in 1881 to a Presbyterian clergyman father. He grew up in Derry, studied law at Trinity College, and had the distinction of being a judge in both the British and Free State courts. Wylie was an avid horseman from a young age and he often competed at the Dublin show. In 1919, he led a protest at the shoddy state of judging at the competition, which had that year experimented with a one-on-one, knock-out format. Dismayed, he set about codifying the rules of showjumping, and his short essay on the matter became the foundation for judging national and international showjumping competitions at the RDS. Wylie himself became the principal judge at the Dublin Horse Show, turning out every year in suit and tall hat to award the winners their rosettes, his Northern accent booming out over the public address system. He gave his name to the restaurant I found myself sheltering outside during the Show.

And it was Wylie who met with two officers from the Swiss Army in the Shelbourne Hotel in 1925 to field the suggestion that Ireland host an international showjumping competition. At that time, Ireland exported between 500 and 1000 horses to Switzerland each year. The Swiss officers thought that a prestige competition would allow the Irish to show off their horses and increase that number dramatically. The wealthy religious leader and political figure, Sir Sultan Muhammed Shah, Aga Khan III, then resident in Switzerland, was persuaded to sponsor the event and in August 1926 the first Aga Khan Nations Cup Trophy was presented to a Swiss team who all rode Irish-bred horses. Over the course of fifty-odd years, the Show had been transformed from a single dramatic jump—an occasion for accessible fun and mild sporting risk—into a tightly regulated, highly competitive five-day festival swirling around one glamorous event overburdened with national economic fragility and international diplomatic intrigue. It became an entirely different kind of spectacle. This new Show was, in part, Wylie's creation and it was judged by Wylie's rules.

*

It's Thursday morning and I am seeking out the warmer pockets of sunshine near the small oval showing rings where horses of various breeds and ages— various 'classes', I should say—are paraded in front of two or three judges. The best are rewarded with rosettes, trophies, and small amounts of cash. People are clinging to the white railings that surround the rings, standing two or three deep to get a look at the Connemara ponies gathered in the centre. A young girl in a glittery unicorn costume clambers up onto the rail. 'It's a danger-free zone!' she shrieks to her sister.

Unlike jumping, which generates a straightforward narrative drama and operates under rules and structures which are easy to understand, showing events are, to an outsider such as myself, impenetrable to the point of boredom. They require a great deal of patience, or a natural interest in horseflesh, because nothing exciting ever happens. Horse after indistinguishable horse trots around the little ring; occasionally someone in the crowd will coo quietly to their companions and point at something I can't see. Sometimes a younger horse will show some resistance and refuse to turn or run the way their owner would like, but mostly everyone is well-behaved and the event is tedious. But this is to be expected: it is not exactly a spectator sport. Nothing is *meant* to happen.

When they're showing, the horse is termed an 'exhibit.' The physical and aesthetic details of each exhibit are captured under four headings: quality, movement, presence, and substance. The aim is to favour 'traditional breeding', but I don't know quite what this means. In many classes, there will be two judges—a riding judge and a confirmation judge. The former rides the horse up and down the ring and assesses the movement and feel of the horse, how well it responds to direction and instruction. The confirmation judge observes the horse's build and its personality. There are other classes where the horses are not ridden at all and a team of two or three judges will sit behind a trestle table in the middle of the ring while the horses are walked and trotted around them. They try to arrive at a conclusion about which one is the most impressive.

During many of the showing classes, sheets of paper are handed out to the crowd. They have the name and number of each horse printed on them and a little box to the side where you can rank them. The commentator invites people to test their judgement against the professionals. If you rank the horses in the same order as the judges, you'll be entered into a draw for a prize. 'It's all a bit of fun,' the commentator says. Beside me, a family are deep in muffled conversation around their piece of paper. Finally, a teenage boy speaks up: 'Mam, pick random ones—that's what everyone does.'

After one class, I get talking to two of the official judges—stocky older men in dark suits, one jovial and quite short, the other taller and somewhat more reserved. They're clutching folders of notes, standing at the muddy gate of the ring, and we're interrupted every few seconds by greetings from people in the crowd. Their job is done, they're eager to be away, but I want the judges to tell me what they're looking at out there, to help me see what they see. I find it difficult to even formulate an appropriate question such is the lack of common language. They can sketch the outline of things easy enough, but it's clear that there's a level of intuition and experience which they simply can't articulate, not to someone like me anyway. 'It's just the best horse in the ring,' the taller judge tells me. He will say no more.

During each event, a commentator reads out each horse's name and lineage, illuminating their sires and dams going back through the generations, noting their ancestors' wins at competitions just like this, years or decades previous. Listening to this litany of historical information is quite soothing because none of it means anything to me. It certainly doesn't make it easier for me to judge what I'm looking at. The commentator's voice is like a chant in some ancient ritual, a mantra that says: even though the horses will change, the comforting roll of tradition and inheritance will continue undisturbed. Unable to pick out the kinds of details that the breeders and buyers around me notice without thinking, I have little choice but to think about the abstract shape of the event; not any specific facets of equine competition, but the social dimension of people coming to the same place, at the same time, to partake in the same activity, as the generations before them once did. There is a kind of mystical sense that what's happening here has been *handed down*. Every time I speak to someone at the Show—rider, judge, breeder, steward—I ask them, *how did you get into horses*? And every person, without exception, replies: *I was born to it.*

*

When the Dublin Horse Show was first organised, horses were still a practical, everyday concern. For their strength, speed, and reliability, they were an essential part of how society functioned, vital to the military and to the agricultural economy. They were a major mode of transport. So when people came to watch horses jump at the Show, they likely did so with prior knowledge and experience of the animals—they knew what to look for, what to expect. People brought horses to the Show for the fun of competition, but they knew also that success would increase their sale price. The jumping, entertaining as it could be, was just a central point around which an entire ecosystem of breeding and trading took place. That ecosystem, in a concentrated modern form, is still in place today.

However, even as the Show established itself, the position of the horse in society was changing. 'Lethal firepower and not flesh and blood horsepower was the future stuff of war,' writes Michael Slavin in his book, *Showjumping Legends*. In the newly industrialised field of battle, horses were becoming more a hindrance than a help. In civilian life, horses would soon be replaced by motor cars, trams and buses. Horses were still valuable to smaller farmers into the 20th century, but that reliance would not last long beyond the invention of the tractor. Even in the 19th century, Slavin says, it was clear to many that 'leisure riding was the future role of the horse.'

The displacement of the horse from everyday life meant an increasing need for spectacle—horses were no longer ordinary, so they had to be extraordinary. They had to be glamorous; a signifier of wealth and class and good breeding. Competitions had to be faster, more difficult, and more richly rewarded, in order to bring out the drama of the event. Today, the breeding and raising of horses is largely an inherited and somewhat nostalgic act, the ghost of a world that, in one sense, no longer exists. It is done for pleasure and less commonly for profit, but rarely is it done for any practical need.

So it is with watching horses at the Show. Because the horse is no longer a practical animal, because it is used primarily for sport, people come to watch and be entertained—they need novelty, character, narrative. And that narrative must be rooted somewhere; in this case, it's rooted in the history and tradition of the Show, and the people who make it possible. It is the riders, the breeders, the judges, stewards, and farriers who best understand the Show's history because they were brought up within its unique atmosphere. This is their inheritance: no one has needed to explain any of this to them; it's been there always, and it is not questioned. The esoteric traditions, costumes and vernacular are the foundation of the whole Show—this is the well it draws on for its integrity, its confidence, its sense of authenticity; the kind of traits that, in a showing class of Connemara ponies, would fall under the ambiguous heading of 'personality'.

At the same time, if the Show is not to become the equivalent of a musty antiques fair, it needs to draw large crowds of people much less familiar with its illustrious past. These are the people who generate the noise in the arena and the buzz around the grounds; the people who show up looking for a good time even though they've never been near a horse in their life; the people who just want to spend a day or two standing quite close to other well-dressed people who may or may not have any relationship to equestrian sports. Money flows through it, of course; from the Swiss watchmakers and high-end carmakers who sponsor the Show, to the horses themselves—the traditional rich-man's folly. The glamour of the Show, its sense of being a notable date on the social calendar, an *occasion*, relies on the sense of spectacle which it can create.

And it is a social spectacle because, as pure sport, showjumping is pretty dire. The rules of the game—as defined by Wylie and others like him—though perhaps necessary and sensible, ultimately reward the competitors who make fewer mistakes; there's little place for the mercurial, the inspired, or the surprising. In their absence, the Show turns its history into its product; it feeds on its own traditions to elevate its standing as something dramatic and compelling. The insiders, those who know horses, who are concerned with horses, they have their own reasons for caring about the Show. For everyone else, it is not loyalty to a particular horse or particular rider that drives popular investment in the events, nor generally any great drama emerging from the action in the arena, but loyalty to the Show itself, loyalty to the grand construction. In a sense, the crowd becomes their own spectacle—watching themselves watching the horses, feeling themselves being watched; this is the only way for the uninitiated, the horse-ignorant, to actually partake.

*

And so I find myself standing in the middle of the main arena during the Puissance, the most old-fashioned and yet entertaining event of the week. In the Puissance, the competitors jump just two obstacles: the first is an unremarkable combination fence; the second is a vertical wall. Though it's made to look like crimson bricks with white capstones on top, the wall is actually constructed out of light wooden board. At the start of the event, the wall is six feet tall—six inches higher than the stone wall used in the first Leaping Competition. Anyone who clears the wall at that height goes through to the next round, when the wall grows a little more. Each successive round sees the field whittled down, until either one horse, or no horses, can clear the wall. Other jumping competitions are a mix of skill, speed, and jumping ability, but in the Puissance, the entire focus is placed on this one hurdle.

The simplicity of the event harks back to the earliest days of the Show, but its scale—the pounding music, the international allure, the TV cameras and baying crowds—is utterly modern. A thrilling, pressurised drama builds as the event progresses, spurred on by Brendan, the evening's master of ceremonies. I meet Brendan shortly before the event is due to start. He's a short, compact man, well dressed in a sharp pinstripe suit. He reminds me immediately of a rural politician. He knows his role—greeting people as they pass, shaking hands, flashing a quick smile, making eye-contact. We're in the pocket at the back of the main arena, watching riders and owners and military officers mingling before the gates eventually open. Brendan's a little jittery because he knows that once the event starts, he'll have to step out into the ring and perform. Showjumping is repetitive and there are long stretches where nothing much is happening. As the commentator, it's Brendan's job to channel the crowd's energy towards those moments that really matter. This is especially critical during the Puissance because the tension is centred on that one crucial moment when the horse approaches the wall.

The riders begin with the simple warm-up jump, a short combination to get the legs working. Then Brendan shushes the crowd as the rider circles at a steady, loping pace around an elaborate floral display in the centre of the arena. For a few seconds there is no noise, just an expectant intake of breath and the sound, determined and rhythmic, of hooves on grass. Time seems to slow as horse and rider face up to the jump. From where I'm standing, just a few feet from the base of the wall, it seems impossible that any horse could clear it. The horse speeds up and, at the last possible moment, makes the leap. The rider lies right up against their horse's neck as the front legs rise over the lip of the wall and the back legs push as hard as they can to achieve lift. They jump almost straight up, and almost straight down. At the very top of this terrible curve, they hang, perfectly balanced and motionless for a tenth of a second, before they come crashing back down to earth. Then the thud of the front hooves on the turf, and a pause—the intolerable wait, half a second at most—until the rear hooves follow with a clatter. Miraculously, the rider clears the wall. The stands erupt. Brendan exhorts the crowd to give the rider even more adulation, even more noise. Those of us in the centre—the stewards, the grounds-people, some photographers—look at each other in genuine disbelief, blowing our cheeks out, shaking our heads.

The Puissance is exciting enough in its own right, but Brendan really shines during the in-between moments when nothing much is happening. After all the riders have jumped in the first round, there is a break. The sound engineer begins to play 'The Wall' by Pink Floyd over the P.A. It's a smart-aleck move, and Brendan is having none of it. 'No, no, no,' he says into the microphone. 'I think we need different music.' He tells the engineer, with the whole crowd listening in, that they should play 'Shotgun' by George Ezra instead. The crowd loves this, and when the chorus kicks in, Brendan leads the crowd in clapping and singing along. The whole thing is so smooth: Brendan gives the crowd what they want and he lets them see him doing it. They know he's on their side.

After the second round, the cameras begin to pick out pairs of people in the crowd, displaying them on the big screen. A heart appears around their faces, and Brendan encourages them to kiss. They do, every time, and the crowd roars its approval, every time. When a rider trots into the arena, Brendan tells the crowd something about them—Jamie has a hearing impairment; in Sweden, Bertram is known as 'the car-thief'. When one of the Brazilian riders, after a successful jump, tears open his blazer to reveal an Irish football jersey, Brendan leads the cheers. He *oohs* and *aahs* when a sad dog appears on the big screen covered in a blue plastic poncho. He quietens everyone in the moment before each jump, drawing the crowd in and making them feel the seriousness of what is about to unfold. And he inflates them again after, clapping and cheering. He's like a bellows, steadily stoking a fire. I think Brendan understands that the crowd are here to have a good time, and there is no feat of equine athleticism that will give them that. There is no judgement, no sense of appraisal, in what Brendan is doing; rather, it's a question of framing, of getting the audience to see what he sees. He keeps his information light: no meaningless historical facts, no smart-aleck references, no inside jokes. Just the minimum required to keep people involved, to highlight the importance of what's taking place without drowning it in pomp and worthiness. He takes the raw materials of the evening—the horses, the riders, the course, the audience—and, in real time, turns them into something dramatic and accessible and fun. For a brief while, we're all insiders. As I make my way through the crowd afterwards, for the first and last time exhilarated by a showjumping event, I'm trying to figure out where the tradition ends and the spectacle begins. I have no answer.

Mid Winter-Day

Light floods and no more.
There is a tree angled in the quivering shadow
of what was, of what once passed when fig leaves
coalesced and shimmied at summer altitude—
Light floods—then there is none but
a halo dim and dimming upon a sleep-ridden
city, her patting first, punching second, the rug
and its noumena of dust. She had not seen
snow, the double iterations, like moths, hurtling
to and buzzing around the life source.
The ground is clear, black folds in the mountains
brushed with white wingtips, as she imagined—
such mercy melting in her mouth, falling gently
along the Giant's hairline on the far post.

Thuy-Chi Le

Frequent Attender

Chris Newlove Horton

I gave my name to reception. Two women I didn't recognise were sat behind the desk.

'O-*kay*,' the woman with dark hair said, 'and is this a recurrent complaint or something new to you?'

'Both,' I said.

'So it's not the itchiness?' she said, a file open in her hand.

'No, no,' I said. 'That was just the start. It's been downhill since then. Problems all over, inside and out. And now it's at the knee. My left knee isn't right. There's a prickly pain in it — like *that*,' I said and I wiggled my fingers around.

'Make a note,' said the dark-haired woman to the second woman, who chewed gum and typed into her computer for a bit.

I removed and unscrewed a ball of paper from my pocket, and started to read out the list of potential problems with my knee, namely tendinitis, bursitis, fractured bones, fibrillated cartilage, torn meniscus, torn ligament, iliotibial band syndrome, and much more, but before I'd really got going, the dark-haired woman's eyebrows climbed up her forehead. She threw the file to one side and strode out from behind the desk through a pair of swing doors.

The second woman stopped typing, looked up from her screen.

Behind me, just appeared, a man was cradling something small in his hands. His face was sweaty and pale. The thing in his hands was a short red stump, that looked just like a human thumb. A severed thumb, but whose? I counted that the man had both of his.

The second woman typed like she was trying to kill the keyboard. 'We'll be right with you,' she said to the man with the thumb.

'What about me?' I asked them both.

The man opened and closed his mouth. He really was pale.

'This man is a *priority*,' the second woman said. 'Take a seat and someone will be with you soon.'

'Soon?' I said, but I knew it was no use.

I took my bad knee through to the waiting room, looked for a chair to sit.

It was half-empty, with the usual sad acts, grey faces, klutzes, junkies, and invalids all awaiting their turn. I recognised a few faces, but I didn't have time to get involved in anyone else's trouble; I was worried about my knee. The pain seemed to come from the inside, somewhere I couldn't see.

I was massaging my knee cap when an old guy grabbed my arm.

'What was happening out there?' he said.

'There was a man had a thumb.'

'A thumb?'

'Yep,' I said. 'A cut off, bloody thumb.'

'Why'd he have that?'

'I don't know. I didn't ask. But I do know he jumped the queue. He's just a cheat,' I said. 'It wasn't even his thumb.'

'Not his thumb?' The old guy frowned and let go of my arm. 'Won't they figure that out?'

'I tried to tell them. But they wouldn't listen.'

'You can't talk to these people.'

'You're telling me. My ex-wife was a nurse.'

The old guy nodded. 'Bet she smelled good,' he said. 'If you don't mind me saying.'

I looked at him. He was small, well-seasoned, probably older than I'd first thought. His mouth was like a baby's, empty and wet.

'What you in for?' I said.

'The standard,' he said. 'A short back and sides.'

'A haircut?'

He nodded again, folded his hands on his lap. 'I've been coming here to have my hair cut ever since the wife died.'

I'd had, in my time, too many conversations with old men about their dead wives; down the pub, pints in hand, they had gone on and on, and every one, bar none, left me miserable, shaken, in bad shape; I mean, really out there, close to gone; I couldn't go down there again.

'How long you been waiting?' I asked.

'Oh, quite some time,' he said. Then he squinted at me. 'Have you got a brother?'

'No brother,' I said.

'That's a shame. You remind me of someone, and the man I'm thinking of was a very good man. Never knew where he ended up though.'

'It's just me and this bad knee, I'm afraid.'

The old guy twiddled his thumbs, which I didn't think people did in real life. I thought it was just a thing they said they did, for pretend. Yet round and round his thumbs went.

I said to him, 'I tell myself, "Next time bring the paper," but I always forget.'

'I've not read a word since the wife died,' he said.

After that, I rubbed my knee, tried not to look in his direction. The pain was a burning now, constant, steady, dead centre of my knee. It was at work where it had started up, in the office, after lunch. On my computer I watched numbers come and go, all day, with my help, and increasingly without it, big numbers turned small, bad became good, the amounts changed, up and down, and I was there to see it all; my computer brought me numbers and my body brought me pain. But did anyone care? My line manager told me to take it to HR, but HR informed me it was a case for Occupational Health, but Occupational Health was just a number you could dial to listen to a robot try to diagnose you down the phone. 'Press 158,' the robot said, 'followed by the hash key if you have the sensation of something floating in your knee.' Press this key, press that; it took hours. And after I'd pressed an indeterminate amount of keys, the robot would thank me and shoot me right back to the start.

The old guy stood up; they'd called his name. Off he went through the blue double doors. Calvin is what I think they'd said.

From the waiting room you could go in only one of two ways, either back to reception and then outside, or on into triage, through a big pair of swing doors painted glossy, wipeable blue. What happened was, the doors would swing open quite dramatically, in this very important-feeling way, and a doctor would appear and call out your name. It was the order in which the names were called that no one seemed to understand.

I went back to reception.

The dark-haired woman had returned to the desk.

'How am I doing?' I asked.

'In what way?' she said.

Back in the waiting room, it was much busier than before. I didn't get how all these people had arrived without me seeing them go by. Yet there they were, tons of them, I couldn't deny it. I'd just found a free seat, when a doctor came out from the doors and called out my name. I put my hand up and went over, but when I got there the doctor was calling out a different name.

I went back to my seat, but it was taken. I explained to the man sitting there about the pain in my knee, and he lifted up his trouser to show me the tent peg jammed through his calf. The peg stuck right in the muscle and came out the other side. It looked like a kebab. His sock and his shoe were crusted with blood.

On sight of the leg, the woman opposite crumpled in her chair; gradually she slipped down onto the floor. I crept away, stepping over two sets of crutches, a cast foot, a walking stick, a bike helmet, a beer can, and a guide dog's behind. I found a wall to look at while staff circled the woman and then took her somewhere else.

Beside the wall a vending machine offered refreshments at an inflated cost. I would not normally be suckered by those things, but the inside of my knee was like a naked flame; tongues of pain licked up my thigh to my pelvis and groin, and hot drips fell behind my shin. I wanted simplicity. Eat, drink, shit, sleep, that sort of thing. The top row was energy drinks, but they'd been loaded with the labels facing the wrong way. It was impossible to tell what flavour was which can. Not that it mattered. They all tasted the same.

Someone said, 'You look like you have a lot on your mind,' but they weren't talking to me.

A small queue had formed behind me so I picked out something green. And as I gulped it down, a fleck began to wriggle in the corner of my eye. I was used to floaters and flashes but this seemed different to that. I turned in the direction of the fleck and saw Moses. He waved at me and smiled.

'I have been trying to catch your attention,' Moses said.

I went over, shook his hand.

The thing about Moses was he only had one hand. Another thing was he liked to dress smart but never wore shoes.

'What you in for?' I said.

'My wife,' Moses said. The stories of Moses's ailments always started with his wife. 'My wife is scared. She say there is something bad on my back.'

'Bad like what?'

'She not say.'

'Haven't you looked?'

'How can I look in middle of my back?'

'She didn't tell you?'

'Of course she did. That is why I'm here.'

'I could take a look, if you want me to. I don't mind.'

'No,' he said. 'Thank you.'

I nodded respectfully and stared at his stump. It interested me, the space that wasn't, but had been, a hand. It looked hard and knobbly, and not unlike a knee. As if reading my mind, Moses folded his arms, tucked the stump up inside a pit.

'You know, you're lucky to have someone in your life, watching out for you,' I said.

'I am,' he said. 'I know.'

'What was it the last time? Your ear?'

'Yes, yes,' he said, 'my wife saw something in my ear. She said it was very dangerous.'

'What was it?' I said.

'I do not know. And by the time I arrived at the doctor it had disappeared.'

He shook his head, as if disbelieving his bad luck.

'And you,' he said. 'What is up with you?'

I tried to, but couldn't, think of my left knee. I couldn't think of my left foot, left thigh, left hip. It was becoming impossible to consider each part as separate from another. It was all one area known vaguely as 'leg'.

'It was my knee,' I told him, 'but now it's all over, spreading, getting worse.'

'That does not sound good. Have you thought about cancer?' Moses said.

'*Knee* cancer?'

'*Wherever* cancer.'

I put the empty can between my feet. 'I hope it's not cancer,' I said.

'Of course,' he said. 'Cancer is a devil.'

'I just need to be seen. I'm so tired. I've been here for hours.'

Moses laughed. 'This place,' he said. 'We are lucky they don't make us pay rent.'

'I need a piss but I can't miss my turn.'

'Listen. I will tell you an important story,' Moses said. 'My brother is a good man but life is hard for him. He think it difficult. One day my brother is on a boat and he feels so sad, he not himself, so he jump off the boat. Into the sea. But he cannot swim! He is in the sea and the boat is going away, leaving him. This is the end for him. But he is floating. Without meaning to. He is swimming. It is natural to him. He is lost in the sea and he find out he can swim. And then later another boat come along and pick him up. They take him back to the shore. He has to go to our mother and our father and tell them what he has done.'

I waited to hear what happened next.

But Moses said, 'You know what I am saying? There is nothing more painful in this world than a shot in the foot.'

'Someone shot your brother in the foot?'

'That is not what happened,' Moses said.

I wanted to tell Moses a story in return. But could only think of the time I killed a dog on Easter bank holiday weekend. It was this bastard Jack Russell we looked after for next door. I came home a bit late, a lot drunk, and as I was trying to be quiet, it started making all this fuss. So I gave it a little kick, and it keeled over and died. I thought it wasn't coming back, but then it started to whine. I put my hands on its throat, wanting to shut the thing up. I didn't want it to disturb the sleepy peace of my home. But my wife and young son came downstairs just as I was wiping my wet hands on the rug. She made me dig a hole in the garden, behind the shed, to bury it in. A full grave. I dug it in the rain. But the rain was heavy, the hole kept filling in. There was more and more mud, and when I managed to get the dog in there, the mud brought it back up. Ruined my marriage, that dog.

I said to Moses, 'I once accidentally pissed on a stranger's grave. It was meant to be my dad's grave, but there'd been a dispute about the payment and he was in a different plot, so I go down the cemetery one night, not knowing he's been moved, and I'd drunk a lot of beer because I was upset and I wanted to give him a full shower, but I got the wrong grave. The grave I pissed on belonged to a war hero, I found out.'

'What war?'

'The Crimean,' I said. 'It made the local paper.'

Moses made a face a bit like a smile and rubbed his head with his stump.

'Do you think I'll get better?' I said.

'Yes, yes,' Moses said.

Then he stood up, because the doctor called his name.

I went to reception again.

'How much longer do I have to wait?' I said.

'Remind me,' the dark-haired woman said, 'is this a recurrent complaint or something new to you?' and the way she said it, the question felt like a test. It had been my knee that brought me in, but was it really something new? The burning was now in my stomach, and at the base of my back. Soon I'd be engulfed. Would they prioritise a pre-existing condition over something new? I couldn't answer with both, that was my mistake before. It could even be this was part of the treatment process. They needed me to admit to an all-over condition, a complete holistic overview. If the whole became better, then perhaps so would the knee. I looked to the dark-haired woman for help. Her eyes were glassy and her wayward brows were penned on. She looked at me, but not at me.

'It's me,' I said. 'I'm not right.'

The second woman typed into the computer again.

The dark-haired woman said, 'It could be a couple of hours. We are currently experiencing an *especially* busy time.'

'I've waited hours.'

She tilted her head, smiled. 'I'm sorry to hear that. But I assure you we're doing everything we can.'

She turned away, walked into the office behind the desk, and closed and locked the door.

'I don't find her very helpful,' I said.

The second woman did not look up from her screen.

She said, 'How can we help you if you won't help yourself?'

I said, 'I've been thinking much the same,' but by the time I said it I'd already walked away.

Back in the waiting room, things had really gone to pot. It was heaving with the clumsy, the stupid, the casualties of life. It was loud. There was hardly room to stand. People groaned and yelled like sheep. A man was knocking on a wall as you would a door. A woman flashed human bite marks up her arm. Two lads, kids really, chucked a small shoe back and forth, over people's heads. It was a child's shoe, although no children were around.

A voice said, 'What's your problem?'

'Busy bits,' came the reply.

Another voice said, 'It's all fine until it's not fine at all.'

'I know the feeling,' someone said.

It was like a Friday night down at the King's Head. What day was it? What time, in fact? I'd lost track. The waiting room did not have windows. My phone was out of battery and I couldn't stand to wear a watch because it became obsessional, checking for the time. Who in their right mind wanted to be reminded of the time? I mean, the waiting room itself had fallen into minor disrepair. One of the lights flickered, the floor tiles were uneven, even cracked, and on the ceiling were ever darker patches where the paint was discoloured. I was surprised it was allowed in a hospital, but supposed they had better things to do.

The pain advanced. My chest lit up with every breath. My insides curled like burnt leaves. I felt like I did not belong in my body, could not live there anymore. I was being pushed away, forced from myself. I wondered if it was possible for a person's insides to be so completely changed that outside and in could no longer co-exist?

I saw Calvin's face, across the room. He looked deep in thought, miles away. I elbowed my way to him and made us both a little space.

'Back already?' I said.

He looked at me for some time, like he was searching my face for something that he'd lost. Then he leaned close to me, got his empty mouth to my ear.

'Need a haircut, don't I?' he said.

And it was true, his hair had grown quite long. White tufts of it jutted out above his ears.

'That was quick, wasn't it?' I said.

'Was it? That's normal for me. Since I was a small child my hair has grown quick as weeds,' he said, mournfully it seemed. 'I feel sorry for them.'

'Who?'

'Oh, I know you,' he said. 'Wait now. Don't tell me. I think I knew your brother. Good man, with a bad knee. Unlucky bloke all in all.'

I didn't have the heart to disappoint him. And maybe I did have a brother. Who could be so sure?

'So what's the matter with you?' he said.

'Cancer.'

'You ought to have that looked at.'

'I'm trying.'

'Aren't we all.'

He had a walking stick with him I hadn't noticed before and he rocked back and forward on it with his arms on the handle, looking not unlike an old gravedigger resting on his spade.

I told him, 'I don't want to die.'

'It's no biggie,' Calvin said. 'I've been dead before. It must have been in eighty-one or eighty-two. I fell out of a moving bus, into the road, and must have landed very badly because I woke up in the hospital two days later and they informed me I'd been dead. For a whole two minutes I was medically dead.'

'Is that different from being dead dead?'

'Nope. It's the same.'

'What did it feel like?' I said.

'How would I know? I wasn't paying attention. I was dead. But later, after being dead, when I was alive again and in the hospital? That part was just like being asleep. Of course my head banged like nobody's business, but if they hadn't told me that I died then I never would have known. It's not one of those things you can know without somebody telling it to you.'

'Yeah?' I said; it was lot to take in.

Calvin put a finger in his ear. Took it out, looked at it. 'Of course my wife's been dead a lot longer than I ever was,' he said.

'Can I tell you something?' I said, a little keenly I suppose, but I couldn't bear to hear of his dead wife. Because if I did then I'd start to think of my own. Who wasn't dead. Who was still certainly alive. She was out there somewhere, in Liverpool, in fact. Relocated; remarried; no doubt still using the same type of shampoo. I could see her coming out of the hot shower, half-woman, half-steam, smelling, as she ever did, of coconut milk — and with that the pain flashed through me, head to toe, as if it could not stand to be forgotten.

Calvin said, 'I said I'm all ears.'

'You know what they call us?' I said.

'Who?'

'The doctors. The nurses,' I said. 'They call us "frequent attenders". Not to our faces, but to other doctors and in their notes. That's what they call people like us. They talk about us like we're an illness of our own.'

'I've been called worse,' Calvin said.

At that moment a young boy stumbled from out of the crowd and into my arms. I held him for a second before setting him properly on his feet. He weighed nothing, it seemed to me, but even though I'd let him go, I could still feel him there.

'Get off me,' the boy said.

'Sorry, son,' I said.

'I ain't your son,' he said, and I saw that he was right. They were close in age, but this boy had a birthmark round his mouth, the skin of it near-white with scars. His face was pale. His eyes were blue or grey or both.

'Give me a quid,' the boy said, 'for a cup of tea.'

He stuck out a pale upturned hand.

I took out my wallet and wondered what it was for, this odd little leather pouch, with a few notes, a few coins, a bank card, driver's license, loyalty cards, some receipts. It was more or less all I had left. I turned the wallet over several times, but the answer never came.

I handed it to the boy.

Snatching it to his chest, he looked at Calvin, then at me. He opened the wallet and held the driver's license up against my face. He looked at me, then at the license. He read the name off it and laughed.

'You've changed,' he said.

Even before I could respond, the boy disappeared back into the crowd. It had become impossible to see people as separate from each other; the waiting room was one body, bound by pain. I had the sensation of something floating in my head.

'That your boy?' Calvin said.

'No,' I managed to say, 'I don't think it was.'

'Never mind. The past's a dead end.'

'And the future?' I begged him.

'Don't start,' he said.

He rocked on his stick, perhaps marking time. Over the crowd came a sound.

'That's me,' Calvin said, but it hadn't seemed like his name. He staggered off into the throng, in the direction of the doors. 'I'll see you after, with the others,' he called back. 'They're already there.' His voice was clear and high above the noise, as if it came not from an empty mouth, but from an opening in the sky.

Exits

Neha Margosa

One day it's here and the next day it isn't. Somehow it's spring still. Tabebuias flower, pink and yellow on blue. Today Lily woke to the news that a girl in Uttar Pradesh was raped and set on fire. She tries to make herself feel something, to imagine something, to imagine that.

By noon, the messages begin to hit.

One says: *Commiserations. Are you cut up about what's happening?*

Thanks, Lily writes. *Thanks, I think we're okay for now.*

She feels her heart get louder.

Then the signs begin to appear. On the third day the metro station near home begins to crumble, seemingly of its own accord. Ceiling paint flakes, settles on commuters. Rust appears on beams, then concrete hail falls. It's concrete cancer, they say. *It's like it decides it's done being up*, Lily texts Mahima. Is the city actually made of mud, as that yogi fucker claims?

By evening the city darkens. Lily stands in her balcony at 4.30pm, trying to remember the last time she saw a sunset. They've had to save power to make up for the years of theft, or so they're telling us. Her laptop goes quiet. No streetlights are left. In the distance the grating of a chainsaw.

Mahima calls. She should be on her way to a show in the centre of town. She never calls. There's a fire at the Square. They're burning everything they can find.

'The vigilantes got my guitar,' she says. She's gentle; she knows how Lily gets with bad news.

'It's in the fire?' All Lily's breath, punched from her body.

A quiet *hmm* on the other end. 'Yes.'

Mahima and Lily met at an outdoors concert on the steps of the metro station one evening, just before rain. Twenty people in the audience, friends of performers mostly. Lily had forced herself outside, had forgotten the smell of outdoors. Now she paused to stare. Mahima was to play guitar and sing, was setting up for soundcheck. Her hair was in a scarf. She wore rings on her fingers, lips, ears, left index-toe. This presented challenges for handholding but made kissing and fucking newly pleasurable. Steel against cheeks, stomach, wall.

In bed Lily still hums for Mahima the few ragas she knows: Jogkauns, Madhuvanti, Bairagi Bhairav. Lovestruck songs of anguish.

'Where do you get all this anguish from?' Mahima teases her. She has always been amused by what she calls Lily's more mainstream impulses.

But they both love the register, the songs about lovers separated by rain, distance, cruel mothers-in-law.

Once, Mahima deep inside her, Lily, melting, eyes brimming, asked her: 'Will you marry me?'

Mahima was so tickled by the idea that her giggles became contagious: 'You want to marry me? We'll settle in a 3BHK by the sea? You'll be my tour wife?'

And so on.

Between giggles: 'You could never marry anyone, my love.'

*

These days Lily settles into bed every night and feels her heart beat harder until she can't remember anything. The single Kurl-on mattress has caved inward in its centre; her back keeps expecting to reach the ground but never finds it. It's 25 degrees Celsius but the fan is on full blast so she can feel tucked in by the heavy blanket.

In dreams, boars emerge from an attic to attack her. They rush forward at her, rip her skin with their tusks, then discard her, losing interest while she lies, still breathing. She hears nothing but the thud of her breath, surely loud enough to draw them to her again. When she wakes up she's lying on the attic floor, waiting for the boars. In another dream her family flees floods that have finally reached them. Lily, Nina, Appa, and Ma have located a thatched-hut relief camp, an old school. Her mother is always alive in these dreams. A mariachi band plays. There isn't enough fuel or utensils. They're pooling toy kitchen sets from the supermarkets. Lily scoops a quarter-teaspoon of dal from a tiny pressure cooker and looks at it, already used to this.

Then she begins to dream about one of the people stabbing Nina while she—the older sister—has to watch. In these dreams they're usually together on their way back from a metro station or the grocery store. In the most recent dream Lily is in a mall. She locks eyes with her father. He's carrying bags of shopping that she knows are undoubtedly for Rachna, the woman he cheated on Ma with. She sneaks into the long passageway that leads to the loos, so they can pretend they haven't seen each other. She squints to tell the difference between the rooms. All three are marked with the same stylish, pencil-skirt-wearing stick figure. Inside, rows of mirrors drive her dizzy. The floor smells of pulao.

The river has become oily. By day eight, no clean water. Lily goes down to the store and fishes out a wrinkled ten-rupee note. It's gone banana-soft from sitting in her wallet for too long, but she's sure Vijay will take it.

'Two litres?' Vijay says.

'Yes.'

'Hundred rupees.'

'Huh?'

'Two-litre bottle of water: hundred rupees.'

Vijay watches her eyes widen.

'No cash,' she says. Red rushes to her cheeks. 'Can I come later?'

'No later,' he says. But he hands her the bottle, an old, dusty thing, green mould growing in the bottom.

As she leaves the store, there's screaming right outside, near the ATM. A woman has defaulted on a loan and five men have surrounded her, landing occasional blows.

Watching them, Lily wonders what she should do. What she can do. Then a woman in a brown sari comes up to her and slaps her.

'Why are you standing alone here?' she says.

Lily returns to her flat, wheezing as she carries the two-litre bottle up three flights of stairs.

By the ninth day, her heart has broken out in a sweat. *Please don't go out,* Nina texts, *they're everywhere. Shruti wore a skirt while she walked to the medical store and word is that two men grabbed her and raped her. There's no lighting in that lane, what was she doing?* As if she should know.

By day sixteen, no music is allowed at all. Every instrument they could find has been burned. It's Mahima's birthday, and, before all this started, Lily had planned to take her to the lake. Now Lily sings *Jiyara mora pyaara*, Jogkauns, and stops when she cannot remember the words of the second line.

Mahima is home early.

The moment Lily looks at her she knows that Mahima has a song.

Mahima is hushed, fearful, her eyes slightly wider than usual.

'I wrote this,' she says, pulling chord sheets from her bag.

'What the hell have you done? Get it out of sight before anyone sees.'

'I know.'

'The fuck are you doing? You know we're not supposed to be singing. Let alone singing about'—Lily looks at scribbled lyrics—'My mons pubis.'

'But I wrote it after last night.'

Lily looks at her. Brown eyes steady. She feels her breath rest at Mahima's clavicle. Last night after dinner they walked and held hands. The bougainvillea from a house spilled on to the walls. Jasmine flowers fell from a tree. They found someone's parked bike to sit on and spoke and sat in silence. Then they came home and fucked, for hours. Quietly, because they expected them to knock any time now.

Lily is alone in the kitchen. She picks over the dal, forms a small black mound of insects. Mahima is in the other room, singing a Brandi Carlile song about a wife: 'Today I sang the same damn tune as you.'

Someone rings the bell, three times before Lily gets to the door, and they are already ringing again; it has to be a man; the ringing bell reminds Lily of her father.

She's wrong. It's a woman. Her sari is brown.

'Come in,' Lily says, and suddenly they're inside.

Last Poem

The dove and the grass share
a genetic relationship.
These things that fit.
I fit with the night sky
where candles manufacture
classic scenes.
There is a constant
banging in my head.
Not sure what it looks like.
I wanted more.
The green light rushing in.
But the light is strobe-like
against the pane.
I am lost inside it
and have been traveling a long time.
My compass spinning.
So I let go of the world
and the world came back.

The sun leaves us homesick.
It is the mundo of existence.
Hangman wait,
I am sick with sunset
as I wait for the past
to recuperate
lines into a beloved.
I awake to a wanting
other than time.
To see past oneself
over here in a poem.
Sound winging.

The world will burst
into green and fall to dirt.
The dirt will green
when the colours come back
into the words
and these colours speak
not for me but for you.
Thinking of all the people
thinking of people
they won't see again.
And so it goes, high noon
where I worry labour
and its discontents.

I hate hubble photos of the sun,
it looks so fucked up.
I mean, look out man,
the world isn't stable.
A dog whimpers
in the house next door.
These elements nature.
The orders of spring,
for instance, confuse
the speech mechanism.
The lodestone came singing
but the breakage
in the signal was permanent.

Middle of the night
electrons hurt most.
This is a metaphor.
Though I hurt and wonder
unhinged by maybe
and wave to the unconscious.
Punctuation like damage.
Damage like applause.
The hum of the fridge
is all there is.
Somedays, truth is.
I don't got a clue.
I was in the midst of death
when I wrote the poem of life.
I didn't know.

Peter Gizzi

Fable Radio

Neal Hoskins

… Super user
Echo
Command1
'Hi send love'
Sleep 310
Sudo echo
Runfile 'deerlands.mp3'
Run, run, run!

………………………

How long?
A lifetime, yes?
Oh really?
Yes, count the days, can we?
Or miss them?
Ha, well what's a day now?
You don't know?
They say there is majesty in light.
And space?

+++++++++++++++++++++
Print ('I miss you.')
+++++++++++++++++++++

Can we go on like this?

We are here, so…

Where shall we go tonight?

You tell me.

Somewhere we won't forget.

Hmm… the little Czech lodge?

Yes, let's do that, let's go there.

Again?

You and I.

For the songs?

Oh yes, songs.

I could hold you for a million years

Aha

Oh yes, the radio.

Driving down the winter wood.

Mist licking the headlight.

Choose, you said.

Choose me, I screamed.

There was wood.

And a stone fire, and a rusty old axe.

Did we hide?

I believe so.

Or we were hidden.

For there were…

So many sighs

The extra embraces.

They floored us.

And tears, oh the tears!

They would jump down the tracks of your skin.

I raved for hyperspace.

You built a handheld time-machine.

We walked.

Yes, the winter was mist.

A woman appeared and said: Your new follower is close behind so—

Be careful what you wish for.
Suddenly, there—
A deer.
We saw deer.
Out in the woods.
Crystal eyes.
The deer.
Our golden deer.
She said: Do you know me?
Can you feel the moon?
Behold the wild.
Behold the wild! we beamed back.
In snow we ran.
And dreamt.
Like infants.
Like twins, entwined.
They once believed that all lost children who roamed this forest—
Stood up to be a deer.

++++++++++++++++++++++++++++++++++
Type ('This is something else.')
++++++++++++++++++++++++++++++++++

When you arrive, will you know when you see it?
There are x10 moons in this our sky.
Outside there is always night.
And there will be the sound of oceans.
And there will be the quiet wood.
And deer again?
For sure.
You'll find our golden deer.

She runs beside me in the night—
She springs beside me in the fields.
Our deer beside us now.

The chamber of the deep—
The light between us in the snow.
Did I see you go?
Were you taken by the mountains, as I believed?
Sat in the car, cried all the way to the next town.
Late November, winter's onset howling in.

+++++++++++++++++++++++++++
Draw ('Luminous wolves.')
+++++++++++++++++++++++++++

We rushed back to our fable radio.
The darkness of the window mist!
Lock down the lodge tonight you say.
We are here, and we are not here—
Mouthing mine the moon.
Do we leave so soon?
Life on earth?

………………………………

Crash
Echo
Sudo
Corrupt file*MP3
Running sound of deerland
Echo
Command2
Sleep31sudo
Sudo echo
Off Keller/mway4621quad
End – erase

+++++++++++++++++++++++
Play ('Keep on loving you.')
+++++++++++++++++++++++++++

STINGING FLY PATRONS

Many thanks to:

Hanora Bagnell
Valerie Bistany
Trish Byrne
Brian Cliff
Edmond Condon
Evelyn Conlon
Simon Costello
Sheila Crowley
Paul Curley
Kris Deffenbacher
Gerry Dukes
Ciara Ferguson
Stephen Grant
Brendan Hackett
James Hanley
Sean Hanrahan
Christine Dwyer Hickey
Dennis Houlihan
Nuala Jackson
Geoffrey Keating
Jack Keenan
Jerry Kelleher
Jack Kelleher
Conor Kennedy
Claire Keogh
Joe Lawlor
Irene Rose Ledger
Róisín McDermott
Petra McDonough
Lynn McGrane
Jon McGregor
John McInerney

Niall MacMonagle
Finbar McLoughlin
Maggie McLoughlin
Ama, Grace & Fraoch MacSweeney
Mary MacSweeney
Paddy & Moira MacSweeney
Anil Malhotra
Gerry Marmion
Ivan Mulcahy
Michael O'Connor
Patrick O'Donoghue
Kieran O'Shea
Lucy Perrem
Maria Pierce
Peter J. Pitkin
George Preble
Mark Richards
Orna Ross
Fiona Ruff
Alf Scott
Ann Seery
Attique Shafiq
Eileen Sheridan
Alfie & Savannah Stephenson
Marie Claire Sweeney
Olive Towey
Debbi Voisey
Therese Walsh
Ruth Webster
The Blue Nib (Poetry Website)
Museum of Literature Ireland
Solas Nua

*We'd also like to thank those individuals who have expressed the preference
to remain anonymous.*

By making an annual contribution of 75 euro, patrons provide us
with vital support and encouragement.

BECOME A PATRON ONLINE AT STINGINGFLY.ORG

or send a cheque or postal order to:
The Stinging Fly, PO Box 6016, Dublin 1.

Darran Anderson is the author of *Imaginary Cities* (Influx Press) and the forthcoming *Inventory* (Chatto & Windus). He grew up in Derry and lives in London. He writes about architecture and cities for a living.

Carol Ballantine is a writer and researcher. She is currently completing a PhD in NUI Galway on the lives of migrant women in Ireland.

Melaina Barnes is a writer and artist from the north of England. Her short stories have appeared in *Litro, MIR Online* and *The Corona Book of Science Fiction*. She lives in Lisbon.

Hayley Carr studied Visual Communications & Visual Culture in NCAD. She is the Visual Arts editor at HeadStuff.org and lives in Dublin.

Anne Carson was born in Canada and teaches ancient Greek for a living.

Tadhg Coakley is a writer from Cork. His debut novel, *The First Sunday in September*, was published by The Mercier Press in 2018. He has just completed a crime novel set in Cork city and is currently working on a book of essays about his lifelong intimacy with sport.

Emily S. Cooper is from the border between Derry and Donegal. She is a graduate of Goldsmiths and the Seamus Heaney Centre and has been published in *Banshee* and *The Irish Times*. She was selected for the Poetry Ireland Introductions series in 2019 and awarded a residency in New Delhi by the Arts Council of Northern Ireland.

Jonathan C. Creasy is a writer, musician, broadcaster, and filmmaker based in Dublin. He is currently an IRC Fellow in University College Dublin, where he lectures in English and Creative Writing. www.jcreasy.com

Jimmy Cummins teaches English in a secondary school in East London. He also writes poems. He used to do a lot more but he can still be found on twitter @defaultpoetry

Susannah Dickey's first novel, *Tennis Lessons*, will be published in 2020 by Doubleday. She is the author of two poetry pamphlets, *I had some very slight concerns* (2017) and *genuine human values* (2018), both with The Lifeboat, Belfast. She is from Derry.

Ellen Dillon completed a PhD in contemporary poetry at DCU School of English. Her pamphlet, *Heave*, was recently published by Smithereens Press and *Sonnets to Malkmus* is forthcoming from Sad Press. Her poems have appeared in *Adjacent Pineapple, Amberflora, Banshee, CUMULUS, Datableed, Para.text, Smithereens Literary Magazine*, and *Zarf*.

Ted Dodson is the author of *At the National Monument / Always Today* (Pioneer Works, 2016) and *Pop! in Spring* (Diez, 2013). He edits for *BOMB* and *Futurepoem* and is a former editor of *The Poetry Project Newsletter*.

Martina Evans is an award-winning poet and novelist, the author of eleven books of prose and poetry, including her latest book of poems, *Now We Can Talk Openly About Men* (Carcanet, 2018). A regular contributor to *The Irish Times*, she is a Royal Literary Fund Advisory Fellow and lives in London with her daughter, Liadain.

Dean Fee is studying for an MA in Writing in NUI Galway. As well as writing short stories, he is also an essayist and is currently working on a novel.

Fergal Gaynor is a poet, critic and editor based in Cork. His poetry has appeared in issues of *Shearsman, The Irish University Review, Poetry Salzburg Review, Free Verse*, etc. A collection, *VIII Stepping Poems & Other Pieces*, was published by Miami University Press in 2011.

Piers Gelly is a writer and radio producer based in Charlottesville, Virginia. His work has appeared in *The Literary Review* and on *99% Invisible*.

Peter Gizzi's most recent books include *Archeophonics* (shortlisted for a National Book Award) and *In Defense of Nothing: Selected Poems 1987-2011*, both published by Wesleyan University Press. For a number of years he edited *o·blēk: a journal of language arts*. He currently teaches at the University of Massachusetts, Amherst.

Louise Hegarty won the inaugural Sunday Business Post/Penguin Ireland Short Story Prize and has had work published in *Banshee, The Tangerine* and *The Dublin Review*. Most recently she has had a short story featured on BBC Radio 4's Short Works. She lives in Cork.

Chris Newlove Horton's fiction has appeared in *Lighthouse, Banshee,* and *The Moth*. He has twice been shortlisted for The White Review Short Story Prize.

Neal Hoskins works in publishing. This is the first story he has written for quite some time. He is on instagram @wingedchariot

Rebecca Ivory lives and works in Dublin. She writes short stories. 'The Consequences' is her second story to feature in *The Stinging Fly*.

John Kelly's work has been published in numerous journals and anthologies. A novel, *From Out of The City*, was shortlisted for Novel of the Year at the Bord Gáis Book Awards in 2014, and a radio play *The Pipes* was broadcast by RTÉ. His first poetry collection, *Notions*, was published in 2018 by Dedalus Press.

Chris Kohler is a writer living in Glasgow. His work has been published in *Gutter* and *Egress*.

A.E. Kulze is a writer from the Lowcountry of South Carolina. Her fiction has been selected by Claire Vaye Watkins as the winner of the Tennessee Williams Fiction Contest and has appeared in *Nat. Brut* and in *The Master Review*'s anthology of 'the best stories by emerging writers' edited by Amy Hempel.

Daisy Lafarge is a writer, artist and editor. *understudies for air* (2017) was published by Sad Press and selected as a book of the year by *The White Review* and The Poetry School. She received an Eric Gregory Award in 2017 and was runner-up in the 2018 Edwin Morgan Poetry Award.

Thuy-Chi Le was born and grew up in Vietnam. She graduated from the University of Chicago, where she studied philosophy and literature, and now lives in Ithaca, New York, as an MFA candidate in poetry at Cornell University.

Fran Lock is the author of five poetry collections, most recently *Dogtooth* (Out Spoken Press, 2017) and *Ruses and Fuses* (Culture Matters, 2018) in collaboration with collage artist Steev Burgess. Her next full collection, *Contains Mild Peril*, is due to be published by Out Spoken Press later this year.

Annick MacAskill is a Canadian poet whose writing has appeared in *Room*, *Plenitude*, *Best Canadian Poetry*, *Grain*, *Arc*, and others. Her debut collection, *No Meeting Without Body* (Gaspereau Press, 2018), was nominated for the Gerald Lampert Memorial Award. Her second collection will be published by Gaspereau Press in spring 2020.

Ian Maleney is a writer from Offaly. A collection of essays, *Minor Monuments*, is published by Tramp Press. He was writer-in-residence at the RDS Dublin Horse Show 2018.

Neha Margosa writes and lives in Bangalore, India. Neha's non-fiction has appeared in *The Toast* and *The Caravan*, and their fiction has previously appeared in *Out of Print*.

David Means was born and raised in Michigan and is the author of one novel and five collections of short stories, most recently *Instructions for a Funeral*. His fiction has appeared in *The New Yorker*, *Harper's* and *Esquire*, among other publications. He lives in Nyack, New York, and teaches at Vassar College.

Eiléan Ní Chuilleanáin is a Fellow and Professor of English (Emerita) of Trinity College, Dublin, where she has taught, researched and written on Renaissance literature and translation since 1966. Her most recent collections are *Sun-fish* (2010) and *The Boys of Bluehill* (2015). She is the current Ireland Professor of Poetry.

Doireann Ní Ghríofa writes both prose and poetry, in both Irish and English. Her artistic practice encompasses cross-disciplinary collaborations, fusing poetry with film, dance, music, and visual art. Among her awards are a Lannan Literary Fellowship and the Rooney Prize for Irish Literature. She is a member of Aosdána.

James Conor Patterson is from Newry, County Down. Writing has been featured or is forthcoming in: *The Guardian, The Irish Times,* and *New Statesman*. In 2017 he received an ACES bursary from the Arts Council of Northern Ireland. In 2018 he was Writer-in-Residence for the C.S. Lewis Festival. He tweets at @JCPattz

Sean O'Reilly's published work includes *Curfew and Other Stories* and the novels *Love and Sleep, The Swing of Things* and *Watermark. Levitation,* his second collection of stories, was published by The Stinging Fly Press in 2017. He is a member of Aosdána.

Keith Payne was the Ireland Chair of Poetry Bursary Award winner 2015-2016. Recent collections include *Broken Hill* (Lapwing, Belfast, 2015); *Six Galician Poets* (Arc, 2016); *Diary of Crosses Green, from the Galician of Martín Veiga* (Francis Boutle, 2018), *The Desert, from the Galician of María do Cebreiro* (Shearsman, 2019) and *Second Language, from the Galician of Yolanda Castaño* (forthcoming, Shearsman 2019).

Dizz Tate has been previously published in *3:am magazine, No Tokens Journal, Prism International, The Tangerine,* and *Dazed*. Her pamphlet of stories, *Nowhere To Go But Back Again,* was published in 2018 by the Goldsmiths Press. She is working on her first novel.

Lindsay Turner is the author of *Songs & Ballads* (Prelude, 2018) and the translator of several books of contemporary Francophone poetry and philosophy. She lives in Greenville, South Carolina.

David Wheatley's books include *Our Lady of the Snows* (Clutag Press, 2018). He lives in rural Aberdeenshire.

Grahame Williams is from County Down and his work has appeared in *The Stinging Fly, The Lonely Crowd* and the Letters Page. He has previously won an Arvon/ Jerwood Mentorship for fiction writing and his current work in progress is about the construction of a giant in the last Belfast shipyard.

~

ABOUT OUR EDITORS

Danny Denton is a writer from Cork. His first novel, *The Earlie King & The Kid In Yellow,* was published by Granta Books in February 2018. His work has appeared in *The Stinging Fly, Southword, Granta, Winter Papers, Tate Etc., The Guardian, The Irish Times, Architecture Ireland & The Big Issue,* among others.

Cal Doyle's poetry has appeared in *Prelude, Poetry* (Chicago), *The Free Press Anthology of Irish Poetry,* and elsewhere. He lives in Cork.